Hanne Sonne

ANGELS
in
Russian Tape Lace

Forlaget Akacia

© 2003 Forlaget Akacia
Skovvænget 1
5690 Tommerup
Danmark
akacia@akacia.dk

Printed at Økotryk I/S, Videbæk, Denmark, 2003

ISBN: 87-7847-070-6

Contents

Preface

The inspiration for this book, Angels in Russian Tape Lace, originates from the absolutely fantastic book with the title Klöppelspitzen aus Wologda. This book contains a fairytale world of lace motives, which abound in Russia. In the middle of this enchanted world, a particular angel caught my attention, and with this as my inspiration, I started drawing different angels.

We all know the expression: "An angel must be passing" when a group af animeted people suddenly goes quit. We often connect this silence with purity and angels – they are white, pure and delicate.

The word angel originates from the Greek word ángelos, which means messenger and is linked to the concept of a heavenly creature who may act as an intermediary between heaven and earth. Here we think of an angel helping human beings. All of these positive conceptions have served as background material for my creative work with angels. This pure, delicate whiteness has been the point of origin.

Lace also expresses delicacy and pureness. The fine threads that patiently obey the command of the skilled lace-maker – and finally a beautiful result emerge: both simple and complex at the same time.

This is my idea of a simple angel – I hope it will bring peace and joy in your heart while you work on it and that the book will encourage you to start making Russian lace.
Furthermore, I would like to express my gratitude to Bitten Andersen who have made many of the angels in this book for me.

Hanne Sonne
October 2003

Tape Lace

Tape lace is one of the most popular types of lace – after Torchon Lace. It is, as indicated by the name, lace made of a continuous tape, twisting to form decorative patterns. At the ploint where the twists in the tape connect, they are sewn together or connected with plaits, false plaits or leaves to create a whole.

Tape lace is made with very few pairs in different variations – linen-stitch, whole stitch and half-stitch. Today the most popular types of tape lace are Russian, Idrija and Schneeberger lace. I only use Russian in this book.

Lace arrived in Western Europe at the end of the 16th century and the beginning of the 17th century. Originally in Russia, metal lace of spun silver or gold thread was used to match dresses of strong gold embroidered brocade.

Until the 18th century, the Russians imported lace from the West and it was only available to the family of the Russian Tsar and to high-ranking noble families close to the Court. Later, it was manufactured in workshops in Moscow, founded by the Tsarina, ornamented with pearls and precious gems.

Later still, the Moscow aristocracy started making their own lace. Skilled lace-makers were invited to Russia from Brabant and they made fine lace for clothing, which was fashionable in Western Europe at that time.

In the 19th century and the first half of the 20th century, Russian lace was of high artistic and technical quality. Many new patterns emerged, heavily influenced by Russian culture and its decoration, typically in folklore applied art and from an inexhaustible source of imagination.

At this point, lace was made with colourful silk threads spun together to a thick thread, combined with a linen thread.

At the beginning of the 19th century, lace-making techniques spread to many provinces in Russia and lace schools and ateliers were established. Here many new motives were designed and produced.

As the Russians gradually absorbed the finest lace, they transformed national and more traditional lace into the Russian lace we know today.

Before starting

Remember to lay adhesive film over the pattern before it is pricked out, as the finished lace has to be starched. Prick out the whole pattern carefully, as this gives a more precise result than pricking as you go. Pull all the pairs tightly together every time a new pin is placed. The result should be a beautiful and even braid.

Press the pins down as the work proceeds – this gives the braid a better shape. Take care when there are 2 twists around the pin. One twist should be before and one after the pin. Both twists have a tendency to gather on the same side of the pin.

For the angel's head decoration of the angel, the gimp pair is only twisted every second turn-stitch. There is no twist at the worker pair when the second tape sews in. This means that after the whole stitch, a twist is added to the workers and they are sewn into the tape opposite.
Replace the pin, take the worker behind the pin and continue without a twist on the worker pair. In this way, the second tape maintains its full width, and all the "holes" following the edge pins are clear, even after a sewing.

When finishing a tape, do not fasten off the threads too tightly. The lace will is starched, and it is only for use as a decoration. The angel will be seen from both sides, so there will be no wrong side.

Techniques

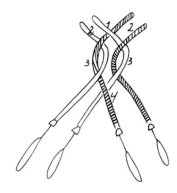

Turn-stitch

1: cross
2: twist
3: twist
4: cross

Remember to remove the pins after making the turn-stitch and carefully pull the inner pair together to make a smooth edge.

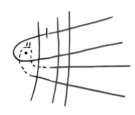

Back stitch

Back-stitch = when the same pin is used twice.
1st time an ordinary double stitch, before and after the pin.
2nd time the worker pair is twisted twice after the linen stitch. Take the pair round the back of the pin (over the edge pair), make a double stitch with the edge pair – and continue with linen stitch.

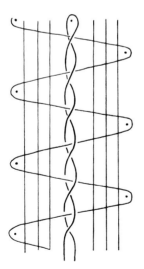

Twisted gimps

Gimp pair laid in for emphasis.

The gimp-pair at the turn-stitch in the glory:
The pair is only twisted on alternative rows on a tight curve.

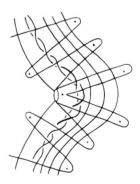

Ordinary four plait

Start a plait with a linen-stitch, then twist and cross.

False plait

For a false plait, you only work with one pair.

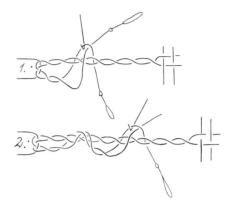

1. This pair is twisted an appropriate number of times and sewn to the opposite side. After the sewing (on the way back) the pair is twisted twice and sewn around the twisted "bar".
2. Two more twists and a new sewing. You can sew once or twice – depending on the distance. The last two twists must be close to the original tape.

Four plait with picot

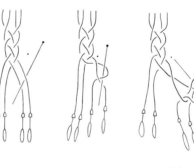

Right-hand picot

Left-hand picot

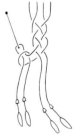

There may be picots on both sides at the same plait. The first stitch after a picot is a linen stitch (preferably) then plait-stitches. Do not make a hole in the plait opposite the picot.

Sewing plaits

A simple sewing with 2 plaits.

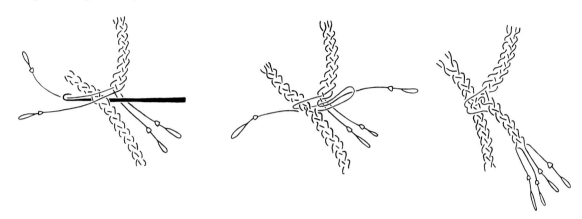

A sewn crossing of plaits or leaves

There are several possibilities for crossing plaits. Here I have shown three methods – and I use them all when apprppriate. Use supporting pins to hold the plait in possition, but remember to remove them before the lace is starched.

Method 1: Put the crochet hook under, not into, the plaits. Gather all the plaits in one sewing, the last time this point is worked. This produces a firm centre.

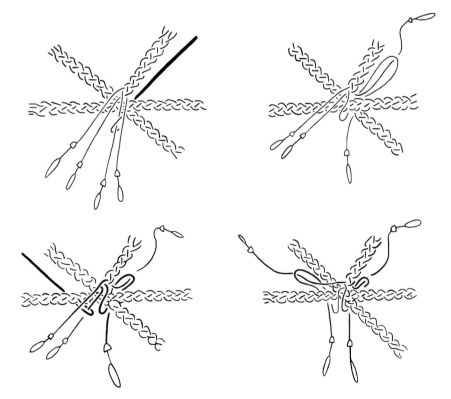

Method 2: This is a good method to use when making a sharp turn round a pin, which is often the case. It produces a good and solid sewing, with one pair making the loop as shown here.
Methods 1 and 2 maintain a continuous plait.

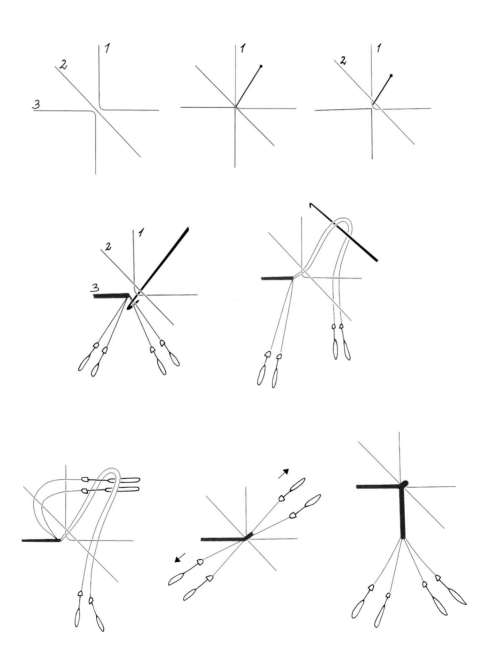

Method 3: I only use this method when it is stated in the pattern. It is more difficult to pull everything together in the centre without making a hole, but practise makes perfect.

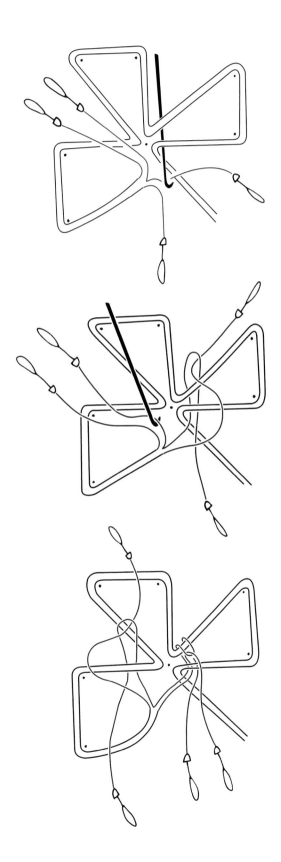

The framework

The framework for all of the angels is the same and is made according to the diagram.

Materials:

7 pairs linen thread 60/2

1 pair DMC cotton perle no. 8 ecru. The pair with cotton perle is worked as a twisted gimp.

Start by making the two leaves in the hair because these lie bekow the work. Finish the pairs off with a small plait, which will be hidden by the tape.

Start no. 2 – from the shoulder, going around the complete figure. There is a start symbol at the beginning of every tape. To finishing off, each pair is sewn into a starting loops and tied off with a knot (a reef knot is sufficient).

Start no. 3 – the glory with 5 pairs. Notice the bottom 3 holes are made with changing workers without pins. Same technique as applied in the tape lace called Idrija.

Symbols

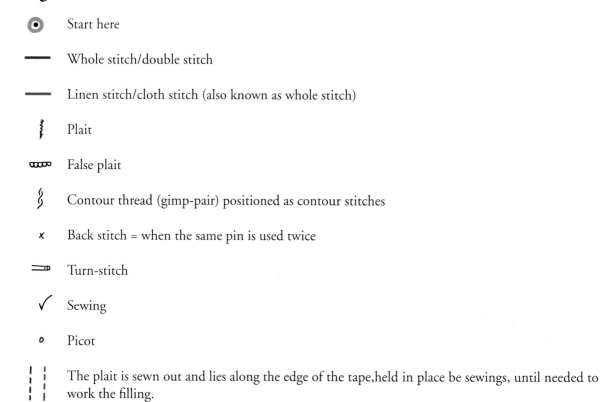

●   Start here

━   Whole stitch/double stitch

━   Linen stitch/cloth stitch (also known as whole stitch)

⌇   Plait

⅏   False plait

⌇   Contour thread (gimp-pair) positioned as contour stitches

✗   Back stitch = when the same pin is used twice

⊐   Turn-stitch

✓   Sewing

o   Picot

⦙ ⦙   The plait is sewn out and lies along the edge of the tape, held in place be sewings, until needed to work the filling.

Filling the skirt

2 pairs linen thread 60/2
Complete the skirt fillings with plaits, false plaits, leaves and picots.

Here are a few notes help you understand the drawing and interpret the pattern markings.
The lace is made in rows, horizontal or vertical, depending on the pattern.

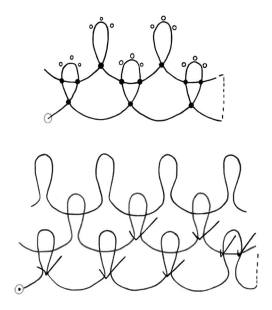

First example: First follow the red line. Place pins on the joins (see the black diagram). In this case, sewings are made where marked by the sewing symbols.
The crochet hook goes under, not into, the plait. Work a linen stitch and tighten carefully, then continue the plait. The dotted line shows where the plait is sewn in and it lies along the edge of the braid, with more sewings as needed to hold it in place. Follow the blue line, sewing into the first row as shown in the diagram.

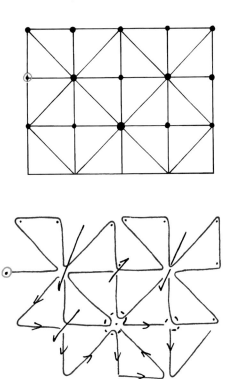

Second example: the black diagram should be seen as a row of squares with pins in all 4 corners. Begin the top row at the start symbol and continue along the red line down in row 2. At the sewing symbols these 2 and the following rows are inter-connected. The dotted line in row 3 means sewing as in row 1. The sewing is made the last time that point is passed, so only one sewing is needed. This is a general rule. It is important that all plaits are kept tight, so a good, firm ground emerges, and they must be exactly the right length, not too short or too long.

When working a filling, it is best to start at a point, and work the entire filling by winding roads, ending back where you started. I have to confess, that I do not follow this rule every time. If the distance is too long from one row to the next, I break the thread with 3 – 4 blanket stitches (see drawing) and start off again where the pattern indicates. A small "roll" of blanket stitches is far less noticeable than a long plait. As I have mentioned before: the angels must float and be admired from both sides. Do not remove any of the pins before the lace has been starched.

Angels never take time off

Angel no. 1

Materials: Linen 60/2 + DMC perle cotton 8
7 pairs linen thread, 1 pair gimp threads
2 pairs linen thread for the skirt filling

Skirt filling:
Start at the green symbol at the upper part of the dress and follow the diagram. Fasten the leaves together when starting the new pair (the blue line).

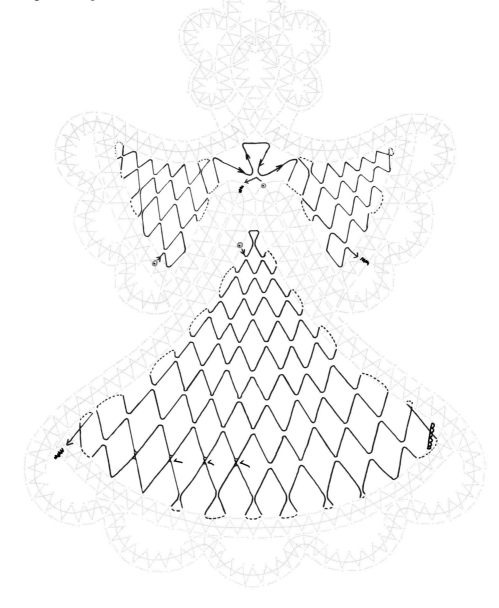

Nobody is as courteous
as an angel

Angel no. 2

Materials: Linen 60/2 + DMC perle cotton 8
7 pairs linen thread, 1 pair gimp threads
2 pairs linen thread for the skirt filling

The filling of the dress is made with plaits and picots as well as a single false plait.
Start at the bottom of the dress. Other plaits start where shown.

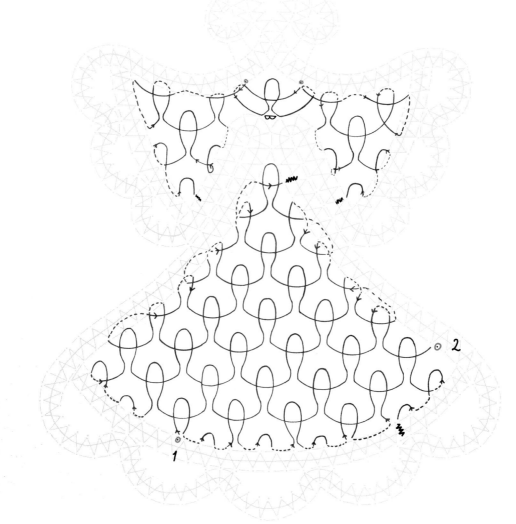

*Send a kind thought to the
angels every time you climb
up the ladder because they are
right there with you*

Angel no. 3

Materials: Linen 60/2 + DMC perle cotton 8
7 pairs linen thread, 1 pair gimp threads
2 pairs linen thread for the skirt filling

Skirt filling: plait with picot.

27

*Under the calm surface,
the angels hide an abun-
dance of deep feelings*

Angel no. 4

Materials: Linen 60/2 + DMC perle cotton 8
7 pairs linen thread, 1 pair gimp threads
2 pairs linen thread for the skirt filling

The skirt filling is made with plaits with picots, starting at the bottom and following the diagram.

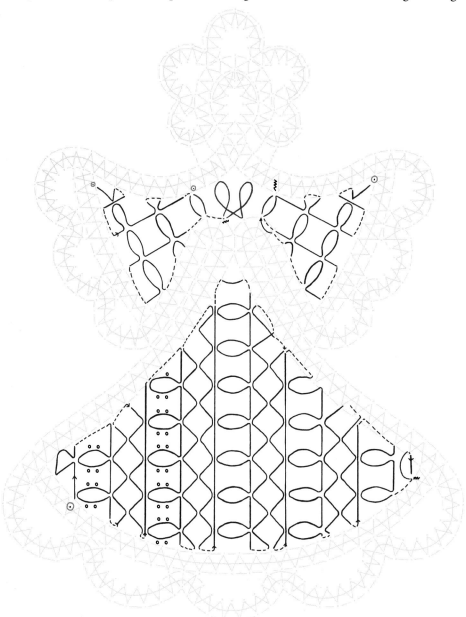

*If you cannot save the
world, at least you can
save your own backyard*

Angel no. 5

Materials: Linen 60/2 + DMC perle cotton 8
7 pairs linen thread, 1 pair gimp threads
2 pairs linen thread for the skirt filling

Complete the skirt filling with plaits with picots, false plaits and leaves. Start at the upper part of the dress and follow the diagram.

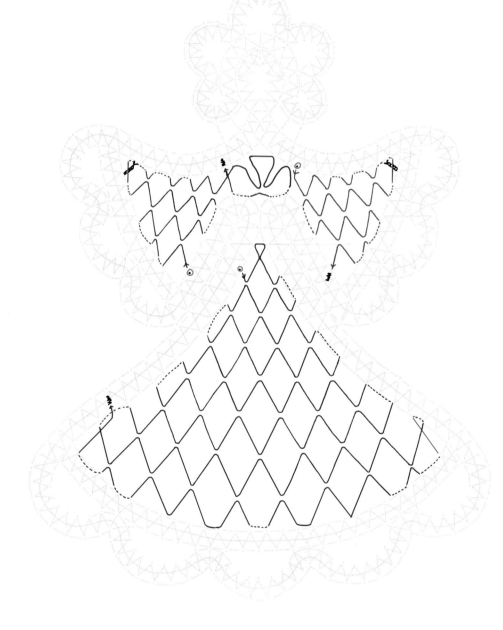

If an angels calls
for you, you must
obey at once

Angel no. 6

Materials: Linen 60/2 + DMC perle cotton 8
7 pairs linen thread, 1 pair gimp threads
2 pairs linen thread for the skirt filling

Complete the skirt filling with plaits with picots and false plaits. Start at the bottom of the dress.

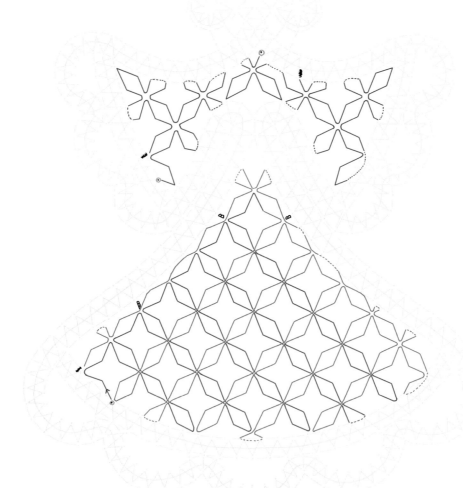

*Always place an extra
plate on the table
– you never know when
an angel might drop in*

Angel no. 7

Materials: Linen 60/2 + DMC perle cotton 8
7 pairs linen thread, 1 pair gimp threads
2 pairs linen thread for the skirt filling

Complete the skirt filling with plaits and picots. Use support pins to hold the shape of the semi-circle.

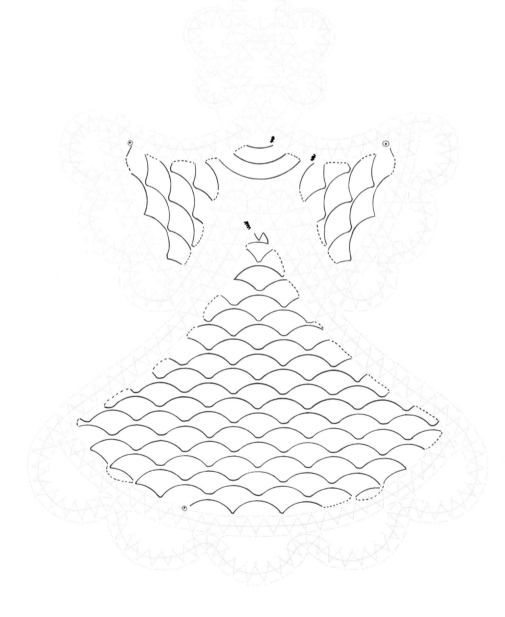

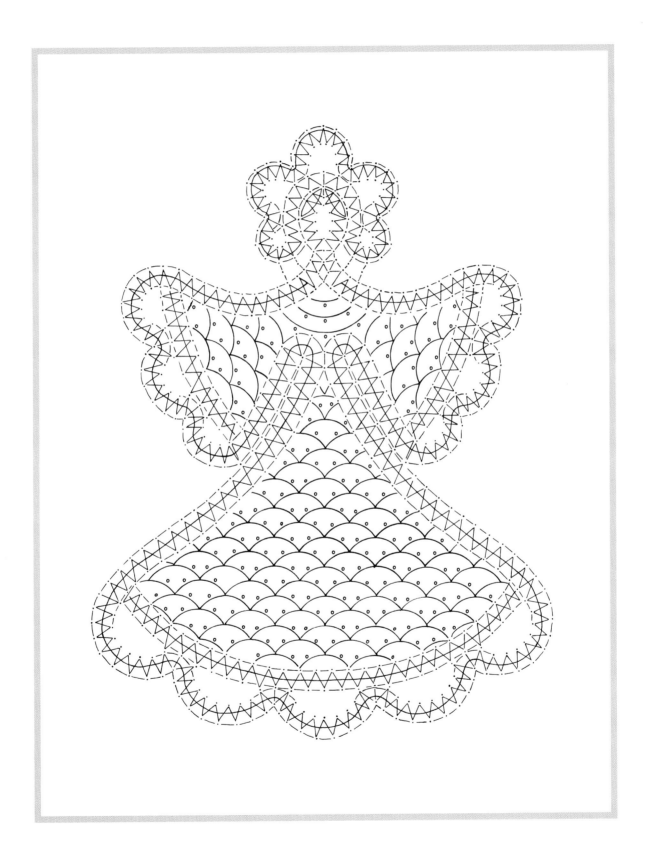

43

*To rely on knowledge is bet-
ter than to rely on chance if
you want to see an angel*

Angel no. 8

Materials: Linen 60/2 + DMC perle cotton 8
7 pairs linen thread, 1 pair gimp threads
2 pairs linen thread for the skirt filling

Complete the skirt filling with plaits and picots.
Start at the upper right corner of the dress and follow the red lines. Then sew into the tape as shown by the blue lines. For the upper part of the dress, start with 2 leaves and continue with the sleeve (false plaits at the tip of the sleeve) then back to leaves 3 and 4. To return to the centre, place a plait on top of leaf 4. Then complete the last leaf. Continue with the right sleeve.

Leave your heart wide
open as the angels do.
A closed heart can neither
give nor receive love

Angel no. 9

Materials: Linen 60/2 + DMC perle cotton 8
7 pairs linen thread, 1 pair gimp threads
2 pairs linen thread for the skirt filling

Complete the skirt filling with plaits and picots, starting at the right corner and dollowing the diagram. Sewings are made with whole pairs.

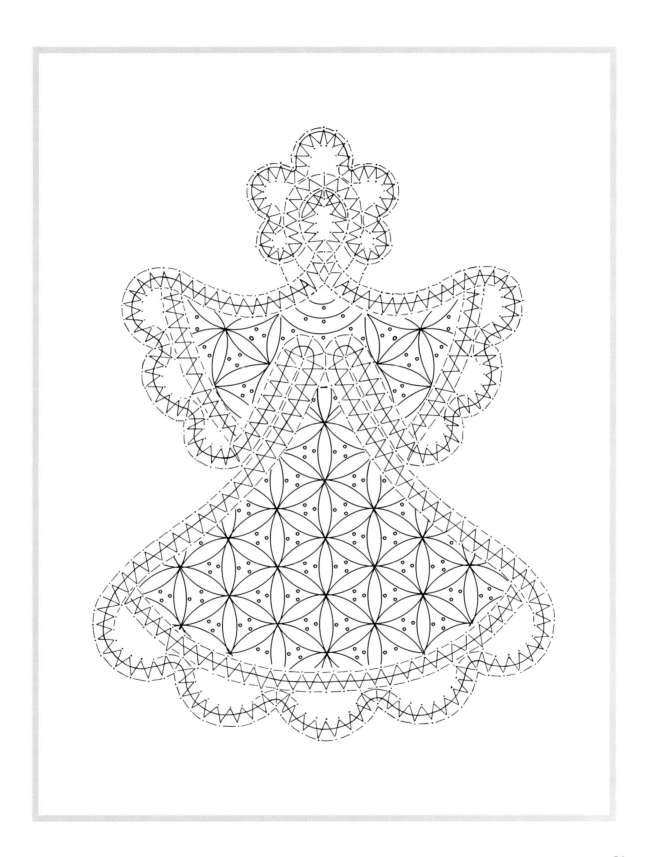

*Fools rush in where even
angels fear to tread*

Angel no. 10

Materials: Linen 60/2 + DMC perle cotton 8
7 pairs linen thread, 1 pair gimp threads
2 pairs linen thread for the skirt filling

Complete the skirt filling by following the diagram. Use support pins where necessary.

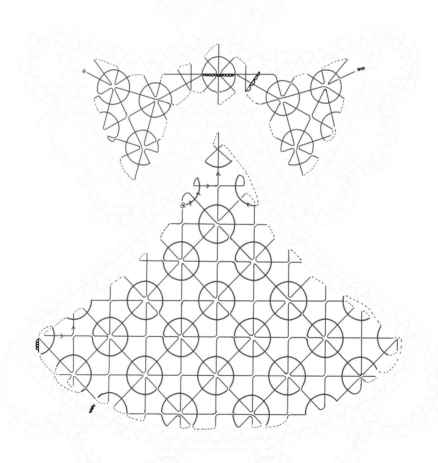

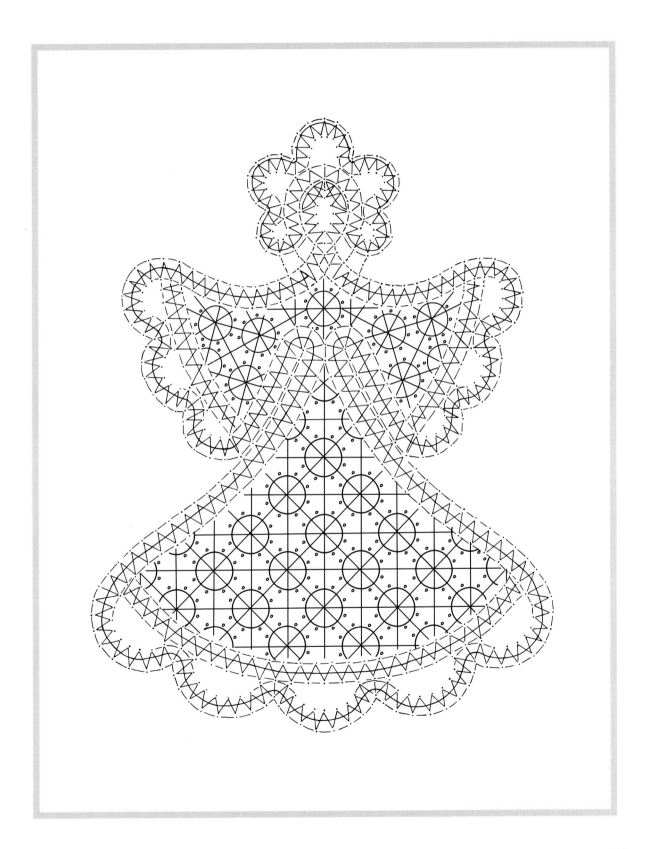

55

*Your guardian angel
guides you and keeps
you safe*

57

Angel no. 11

Materials: Linen 60/2 + DMC perle cotton 8
7 pairs linen thread, 1 pair gimp threads (perle cotton)
2 pairs linen thread for the skirt filling

Complete the skirt filling with plaits and picots, starting at the bottom. Use support pins for the circles.

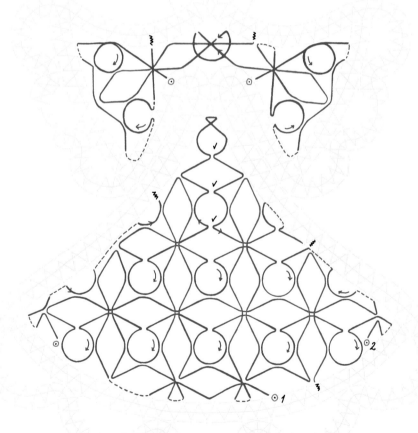

59

Life is a tapestry: we are the
threads, angels are the shuttle
and God is the weaver.
Only the weaver sees the
complete picture.

Angel no. 12

Materials: Linen 60/2 + DMC perle cotton 8
7 pairs linen thread, 1 pair gimp threads
2 pairs linen thread for the skirt filling

Work the dress as shown in the diagram. Make sewings with a whole pair.

63

*Your guardian angel started working
the day you were conceived
– not the day you were born*

Angel no. 13

Materials: Linen 60/2 + DMC perle cotton 8
7 pairs linen thread, 1 pair gimp threads
2 pairs linen thread for the skirt filling

Work the skirt filling as shown in the diagram, statting at the bottom. Make sewings with a whole pair.

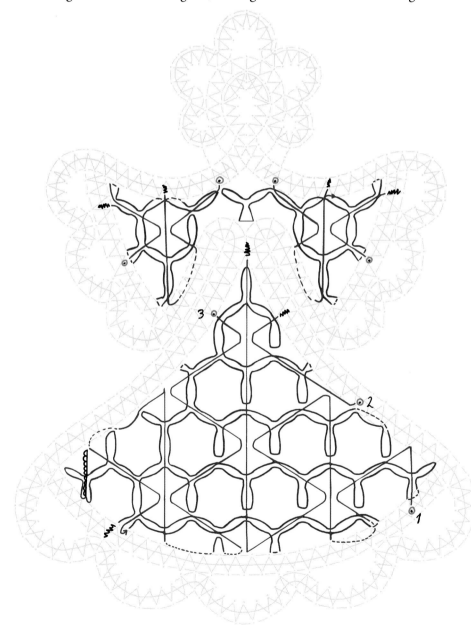

Angels are never
closer to us than when
we are broken-hearted
and sad

Angel no. 14

Materials: Linen 60/2 + DMC perle cotton 8
7 pairs linen thread, 1 pair gimp threads
2 pairs linen thread for the skirt filling

Work the skirt with plaits and picots together with false plaits and leaves.

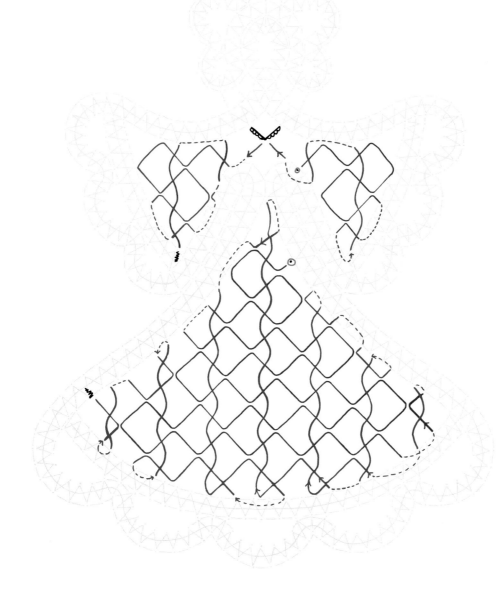

71

Angels are able to fly
because they do not
carry any burden

Angel no. 15

Materials: Linen 60/2 + DMC perle cotton 8
7 pairs linen thread, 1 pair gimp threads
2 pairs linen thread for the skirt filling

Work the skirt filling as shown in the diagram.

Angels do not need wings.
They fly high on the warm
airstreams of love

Angel no. 16

Materials: Linen 60/2 + DMC perle cotton 8
7 pairs linen thread, 1 pair gimp threads
2 pairs linen thread for the skirt filling

Work the skirt filling with plaits, false plaits and leaves, following the diagram.

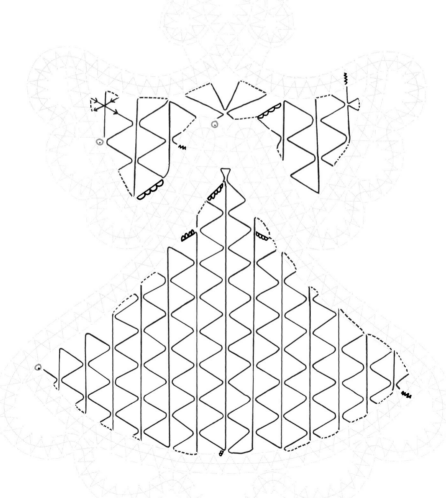

THE CORAL TRIANGLE

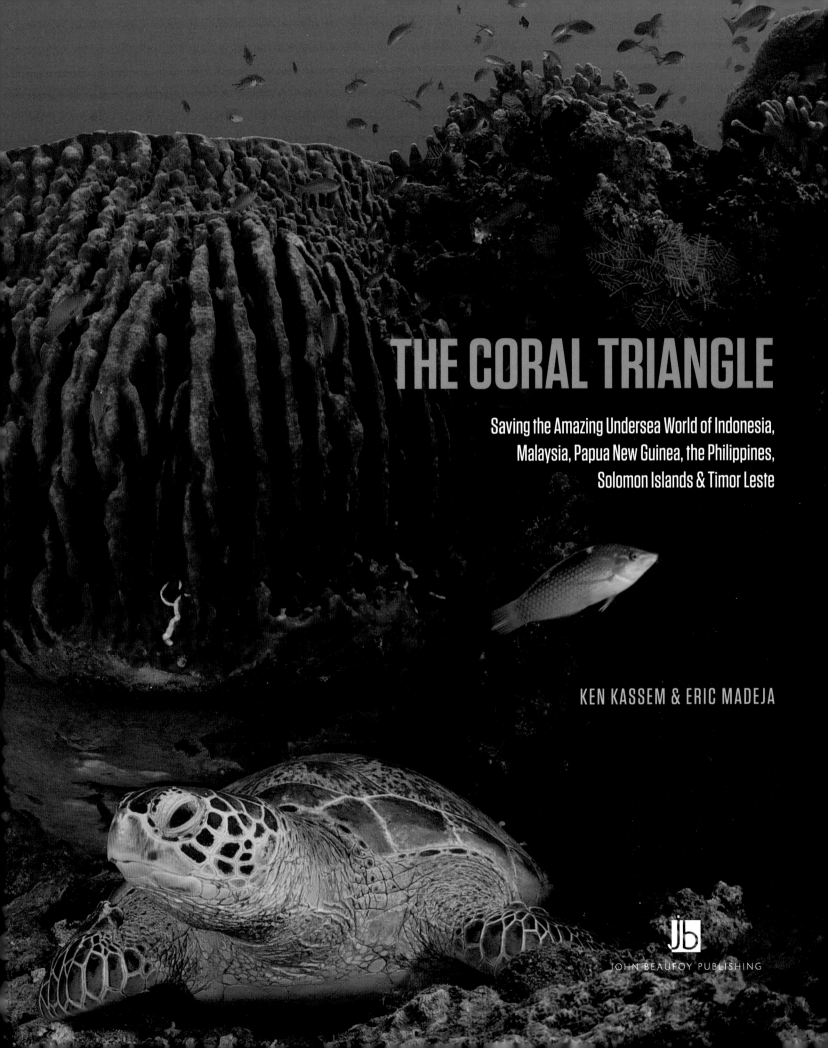

THE CORAL TRIANGLE

Saving the Amazing Undersea World of Indonesia,
Malaysia, Papua New Guinea, the Philippines,
Solomon Islands & Timor Leste

KEN KASSEM & ERIC MADEJA

JOHN BEAUFOY PUBLISHING

*This book is dedicated to the people of the Coral Triangle who have
shown us hospitality and friendship for nearly two decades and openly
provided us with an insight into their cultures and lifestyles.*

CONTENTS

Opposite: Pink Anemonefish (*Amphiprion perideraion*) are sequential hermaphrodites, born as males but changing to females as they age. They often live symbiotically with Ritteri Anemones (*Heteractis magnifica*).

Title pages: Green Sea Turtles (*Chelonia mydas*) are globally endangered but common around Malaysia's Sipadan Island and a major tourist attraction. They often rub against sponges, a behaviour to help them clean barnacles and other organisms from their shells.

PREFACE

THE science-fiction author Arthur C. Clarke once said, 'How inappropriate to call this planet Earth when it is quite clearly Ocean'. It is no wonder as our blue ocean covers roughly 71 per cent of the Earth's surface and contains 97 per cent of the planet's water.

Yet less than 5 per cent of this body of blue water has been explored. This very ocean – on which humans depend for food, commerce, transportation and ecosystem services – is facing serious threats. Coral reefs are being destroyed by overfishing, destructive fishing, inappropriate development and climate change. Turtles and terrapins are endangered, and their populations continue to decline. Fish stocks and other seafood are declining throughout the world.

However, there is hope; a large portion of this threatened ocean can be protected. An important area nestled between the Indian and Pacific Oceans is the Coral Triangle. Its boundaries are defined by marine areas containing 500 or more species of coral and it is the world's centre of marine life diversity. In some areas it has over 600 coral species (more than 75 per cent of all known coral species), 53 per cent of the world's coral reefs, 3,000 fish species and the greatest extent of mangrove forests of any region in the world. Sometimes referred to as 'the world's centre of marine biodiversity', the Coral Triangle is comparable to and perhaps even surpasses the Amazon and Congo Basins in numbers of species. In addition, the Coral Triangle serves as the spawning and juvenile growth area for what is probably the largest tuna fishery in the world.

The triangular-shaped Coral Triangle region covers all or parts of the exclusive economic zones of six countries: Indonesia, Malaysia, Papua New Guinea, the Philippines, the Solomon Islands and Timor Leste. The governments of these six countries have signed a pact to protect and sustainably manage this nursery of the seas – the Coral Triangle Initiative for Coral Reefs, Fisheries and Food Security (CTI-CFF).

I applaud the foresight of the Malaysian Government, along with the other five participating countries, in being part of this noble approach to protect and conserve the Coral Triangle – the nursery of the world. Malaysia is fully committed to this initiative by becoming the first country to ratify the agreement and to establish CTI-CFF's permanent secretariat in Indonesia. The state of Sabah, being the focus of the CTI-CFF in Malaysia, will benefit from this initiative, and I congratulate the government of Sabah for its dedication to translate this to the ground, in continuously engaging all stakeholders to be part of this initiative. The Government of the State of Sabah is encouraging private-public partnerships under this initiative.

I am also happy to see the proactive involvement of local communities in protecting our marine resources and habitats. Local groups in Pitas, Banggi and Semporna are monitoring and reporting fish-bombing activities around their waters. Fishing using bombs home-made from fertilizers is highly destructive to our marine ecosystem. It is destroying reef areas that are not only important to the livelihood of fishermen, but also vital to the tourism industry in Sabah. Therefore, as the then Chairman of the Sabah Tourism Board, I was pleased that the Sabah Ministry of Tourism, Culture and Environment took a positive step in forming the Sabah Anti-Fish Bombing Committee that subsequently held numerous awareness activities at the district and state levels, including the 2012 Regional Anti-Fish Bombing Symposium held in Kota Kinabalu. I am proud to have played a part in combating fish-bombing activities in Sabah, and hope that many more local communities and the private sector can join forces to eradicate fish bombing in Sabah and throughout the Coral Triangle.

Sabah is well on its way towards gazetting more than 10 per cent of its waters as marine parks. Sabah Parks manages four marine parks with three more soon to be gazetted. One of the proposed three parks was declared to be protected in 2003 by the Sabah State Government. Measuring almost one million hectares, the proposed Tun Mustapha Park (TMP) is named after one of Malaysia's founding fathers.

Sabah Parks has been steadily progressing to make TMP's gazettement a reality by the year 2015. When established, TMP will support the CTI-CFF goals by protecting marine biodiversity and addressing climate change; contribute to the post-2015 development agenda and Sustainable Development Goals; as well as contribute to the Aichi Biodiversity Target of at least 10 per cent protected and managed marine areas.

Produced in association with WWF-Malaysia, this book highlights some of the amazing and unique marine features of the Coral Triangle countries. The stories contained in it are examples of the conservation and management efforts of each of the Coral Triangle countries. I hope you enjoy reading it and learning from it as much as I have.

The duo behind this book, author Kenneth Kassem and photographer Eric Madeja, are not natives to the Coral Triangle but they might as well be. Having both lived for over a decade in Borneo – the Malaysian corner of the Coral Triangle – Ken and Eric are no strangers to its shores. Captivated by the beauty and mysteries contained within this coral treasure chest of biodiversity, they adventured together to record and photograph their personal discoveries in the hope of inspiring many others to understand and commit to safeguarding the Coral Triangle region.

As I often say, you cannot save what you do not love. You cannot love what you do not know. This book helps us to know, love and ultimately save the Coral Triangle.

Dato' Seri Tengku Zainal Adlin
President
WWF-Malaysia

Left: A newly hatched Hawksbill Turtle (*Eretmochelys imbricata*) ventures into the open sea. Turtles are not confined by national boundaries and require all countries in their range to engage in conservation efforts.

FOREWORD

THE Coral Triangle is aptly described as one of the biodiversity hotspots in the world today. The area supports a highly diverse marine flora and fauna shared by several countries. The diverse types of habitat found along the coasts of the islands have attracted myriads of species, many of which are economically important and on which thousands of generally impoverished people depend as sources of food and livelihood. During the last few decades, however, the production capacities of these fishery resources have significantly diminished due to the unmanaged and unregulated exploitation of the resources. The urgent need to manage and conserve these resources is the primary concern of the governments within the Coral Triangle.

Biodiversity is the base of life in all ecosystems. The authors of this book are concerned about the possible adverse effects of the loss of biodiversity caused by the increasing pressure on the resources by the people who depend mainly on them. They fear that the loss of biodiversity may lead to the eventual extinction of keystone species in the marine ecosystem. The book also tells of the different conservation efforts that are being carried out by the governments, non-governmental organizations and the private sector in the countries of the Coral Triangle. The different approaches and methods used by these groups are interesting and make good reading for those who are engaged in conservation works.

With the implementation of the conservation programmes and the protection and conservation of coastal fisheries, it is expected that the area's resources will recover to their former productive status in the near future. Alternative sources of livelihood for any displaced fishing families must be implemented so that they can earn enough for their needs. Seaweed farming is known as the most productive and environmentally friendly alternative livelihood for coastal populations.

To provide examples of the conservation projects and programmes of the different countries in the Coral Triangle the authors have gathered information from both published documents and interviews with the people in charge of the implementation of the conservation efforts. The book also includes sections describing the structure, function and beauty of pristine marine ecosystems.

This book on the Coral Triangle is a must; beautiful and informative reading material for people from all walks of life.

Gavino C. Trono, Jr, PhD
Professor Emeritus and National Scientist

Dr Trono was awarded the rank and title of National Scientist by President Benigno S. Aquino III of the Philippines in recognition of his work in the field of tropical marine phycology: seaweed biodiversity, biology, ecology and culture, developed during his 40-year scientific career. He is currently affiliated with Food and Agricultural Organization (FAO) Aquaculture Seaweed Research and Development as technical consultant.

Above: Communities can earn a living income from culturing seaweed as an alternative to fishing and harvesting from the reefs.

Opposite: Orange Cup Corals (*Tubastraea coccinea*) are non-zooxanthellate corals. They usually occupy shaded habitats under overhangs in caverns and in wrecks.

Acronyms

WWF World Wide Fund for Nature
TNC The Nature Conservancy
WCS Wildlife Conservation Society
NGO non-governmental organization
CTI Coral Triangle Initiative
CTI-CFF Coral Triangle Initiative on Coral Reefs, Fisheries and Food Security
CITES Convention on International Trade in Endangered Species
IUCN International Union for Conservation of Nature and Natural Resources

1

INTRODUCTION *to*
the CORAL TRIANGLE

Nestled in the seam between the Pacific and Indian Oceans lies an immense archipelago. Some of its islands are mere sandy specks that disappear with every high tide, while others are much larger – among these are the second and third largest islands in the world. Deep sea basins, shallow continental shelves and warm, shallow waters support the largest concentration of coral reefs in the world, helping to make the Coral Triangle one of the greatest centres of biodiversity on Earth. The Coral Triangle is home to 363 million people, 141 million of whom live within 30 km (19 miles) of a coral reef. It faces many threats, yet even though its habitats are fragile and show signs of breaking under the pressures exerted by humans, there is reason to hope. Governments, businesses and civil society both in the region and around the world are realizing the potential that they are losing, and working to stop the threats and reverse the degradation.

Left: Tufi's tropical fjords, like most coastlines of the Coral Triangle, are lined with fringing reefs that form one of the biggest and richest habitats in the region.

THE CORAL TRIANGLE

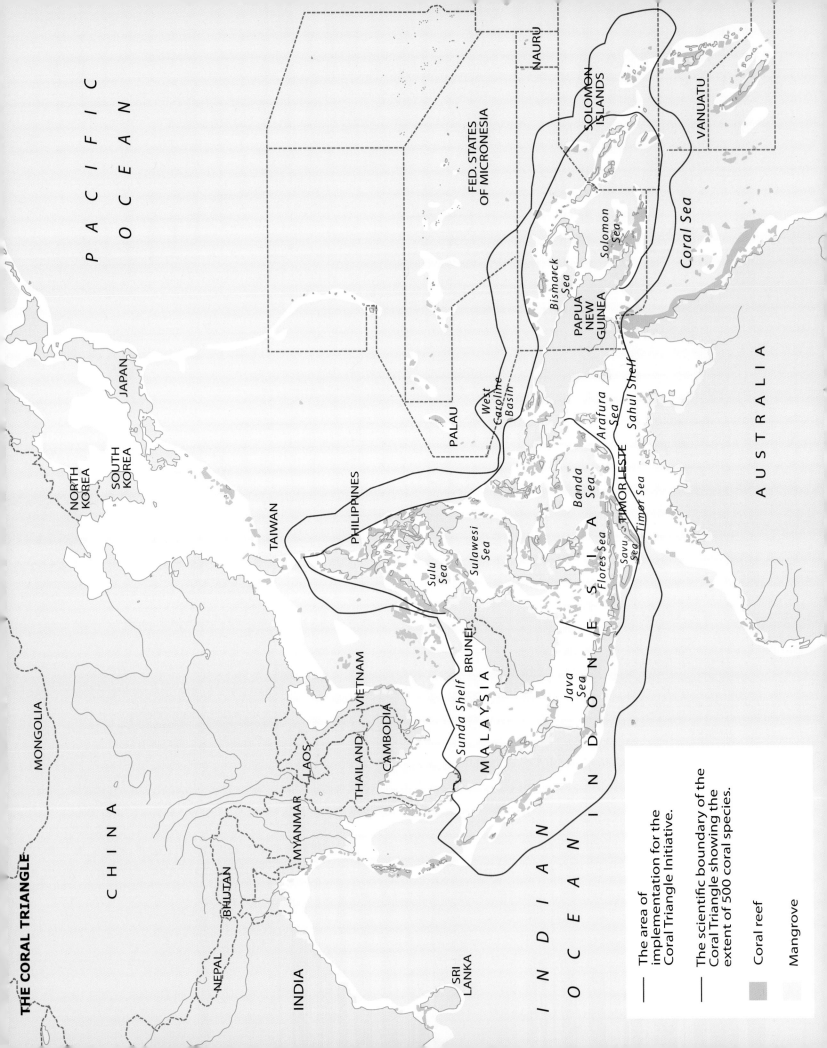

PACIFIC OCEAN

INDIAN OCEAN

MONGOLIA

CHINA

JAPAN

NORTH KOREA

SOUTH KOREA

NEPAL

BHUTAN

INDIA

MYANMAR

LAOS

VIETNAM

THAILAND

CAMBODIA

SRI LANKA

MALAYSIA

BRUNEI

Sunda Shelf

TAIWAN

PHILIPPINES

PALAU

FED. STATES OF MICRONESIA

NAURU

SOLOMON ISLANDS

VANUATU

PAPUA NEW GUINEA

West Caroline Basin

Bismarck Sea

Solomon Sea

Coral Sea

Sulu Sea

Sulawesi Sea

I N D O N E S I A

Java Sea

Flores Sea

Banda Sea

Savu Sea

Timor Sea

TIMOR LESTE

Arafura Sea

Sahul Shelf

AUSTRALIA

The area of
implementation for the
Coral Triangle Initiative.

The scientific boundary of the
Coral Triangle showing the
extent of 500 coral species.

Coral reef

Mangrove

Unlike the other two great centres of biodiversity, the Amazon and Congo Basins, the Coral Triangle does not have physical boundaries. The Congo and Amazon are relatively well-defined geophysical features delineated by ridges and the drainage that results in the biggest rivers in the world. There are no such features in the Coral Triangle, and where it begins and ends is a matter of debate among scientists and conservationists. However, not under debate is the fact that as taxonomists mapped and catalogued the occurrences of species it became clear that this archipelago was special for its high species counts in nearly every marine plant and animal group they studied.

It is now generally agreed that six countries form the core of the Coral Triangle; it comprises parts of Indonesia, Malaysia, Papua New Guinea, the Philippines, the Solomon Islands and Timor Leste. Further west, east, north and south the species counts decrease, but where should the line be drawn? Within the Coral Triangle it is relatively easy to find areas harbouring more than 605 species of hard coral – the building blocks of marine biodiversity. By comparison, Australia's Great Barrier Reef, just south of New Guinea, may be the biggest reef complex in the world, but it hosts fewer than 500 coral species. On the other side of the globe the Caribbean Sea can boast only 61 species. The high species counts also apply to other major marine taxa. Besides corals, fish, mangroves, seagrasses and some shrimp families all find their global maxima in the Coral Triangle.

Above: Harlequin Shrimp (*Hymenocera elegans*) usually live in pairs and feed exclusively on starfish. They can help control outbreaks of the coral-consuming Crown-of-thorns Starfish (*Acanthaster planci*).

Top: Shallow reefs receive the most light and can form spectacular formations. These shallow reefs are perfect for snorkelling and house a vast number of species.

The BOOK'S FOCUS

THIS book is intended to raise awareness of the Coral Triangle. It presents an overview of the marine resources that make the Coral Triangle special, and provides an idea of some of the actions that are being taken to try to manage, conserve and save these resources for the future. The images and stories relate to the riches of the area and document some of the threats facing it, and the text highlights and celebrates the work being done to save the Coral Triangle's marine resources and the people who depend upon them. The world's largest conservation organizations – World Wide Fund for Nature (WWF), The Nature Conservancy (TNC), Conservation International and Wildlife Conservation Society (WCS) – all have the Coral Triangle within their sets of global priorities. The governments of the region signed an accord among themselves to collaborate on conservation and management measures. Local communities and the private sector are also contributing significantly to the outcome.

Conservation was once about saving the world's biodiversity from the onslaught of the current extinction crisis. It has since grown to encompass not only prevention of extinction, but also the sustainable use of resources. In many cases communities living in the Coral Triangle rely on the marine resources and do not have the luxury of putting them off limits to all uses. Fortunately, many aspects of marine conservation have the benefit of maintaining biodiversity and supporting sustainable fishing.

The examples and conservation stories featured in this book constitute merely a selection of some conservation and management projects from each of the six countries in the Coral Triangle. They are not comprehensive reviews of projects or programmes undertaken throughout the area – there are too many of these to enable them to be described in a single book.

Where possible, efforts have been made to verify what is written about each project with information from published

documents and interviews with key people at each project site. Each chapter additionally describes some of the actions that are included in each country's Coral Triangle Initiative (CTI) National Plan of Action (see page 33). The intention is to provide an idea of what each country perceived as its priority at the time that the CTI was signed and the national plans were developed (2009–2010). Neither judgements nor assessments on how each plan was implemented are provided.

The work of non-governmental organizations (NGOs) and the private sector receives more of a focus than do government initiatives; both large international groups and smaller local initiatives receive a balanced coverage. The stories provide an idea of what large and small NGOs are doing to save the Coral Triangle. The people working on these efforts, whether government employees, NGO staff or from the private sector, are struggling to combat some of the biggest threats to our planet's biodiversity, and they all deserve our appreciation and gratitude for their efforts.

Above: Anchovies form massive shoals around Indonesia's Raja Ampat every September.

Opposite: The reef top at the Philippine's Tubbataha Reefs Natural Park. One of the most successful parks in the Coral Triangle, Tubbataha still faces many threats.

BIODIVERSITY

BIODIVERSITY is the accumulation of not only species, but also their habitats and their genes. Even the Greek philosopher Aristotle realized that plant and animal life was not spread evenly across the world. However, it was not until the 18th and 19th centuries that patterns of biodiversity on Earth started to be understood.

SPECIES

Most people equate biodiversity with numbers of species. An area known to have high biodiversity usually exhibits high species counts – of mammals, birds, reptiles, amphibians, insects, fish, plants and other organisms. Species counts tend to be higher as latitude decreases towards the Equator into warmer and less variable climates than elsewhere. Areas with many environmental niches and highly productive vegetation allow species to specialize and eventually evolve into new species.

On land, geographic features often define species ranges. A large river may block some monkeys from reaching the opposite bank, but when a few do manage to cross, a separate species may eventually evolve on the far side as genetic mutations build within the isolated population. When species are isolated on small islands they tend to adapt to the new environment and evolve into new species. Such isolated species, found only in one place, are known as endemics. Thus species richness and endemism are two important concepts of biodiversity. A tropical rainforest may have a high richness of species and be important for conservation, while a small island may be the only place where a certain bird is found and thus also be highly important.

Coral reefs are the most species-rich marine habitat. Even though they occupy less than 1 per cent of the oceans, up to 25 per cent of all the world's fish are found on coral reefs. As much as 37 per cent of the world's coral-reef fish and 76 per cent of coral species are found in the Coral Triangle.

HABITATS

Biodiversity is also the richness of habitats. While 50 per cent of the world's terrestrial biodiversity is found in the tropics, the other half is spread around the temperate and polar regions (Olson & Dinerstein, 1998). In order to maintain the planet's biodiversity, we must conserve representative examples of each habitat type with examples in different regions.

In the late 1990s scientists from WWF created a map of the world to help conservationists ensure that the full range of the planet's habitats and species was conserved. The map subdivided the world into major biogeographic realms (Africa, the Neotropics, the Paleotropics and the Indo-Pacific), with major habitat types nested within the realms (Olson & Dinerstein, 1998). The conservationists delineated ecoregions within each habitat type based on the range and number of species, to form the basic units

of biodiversity representation on land. While they were unable at the time to delineate a global set of marine ecoregions, some clearly identifiable marine ecoregions were prioritized, including two in what would soon become more widely known as the Coral Triangle. The Sulu Sulawesi Marine Ecoregion and the Bismarck Solomon Seas Ecoregion were two of WWF's initial 200 most important places on the planet, and represented an important tropical marine habitat.

Within the Coral Triangle the best-known and most productive habitats include coral reefs, seagrass beds and mangroves. Associated with these coastal habitats are important deep-sea areas, ocean trenches, seamounts and migratory passages for an assortment of endangered animals like whales, dolphins and turtles.

Above: Mangroves and corals are often found near to each other and many species use both habitats in certain stages of their lives.

Opposite: A healthy reef can have hundreds of species of fish and coral packed into a very small area. The corals provide a huge range of habitats and niches filled by fishes, invertebrates, algae and other taxa.

GENES

The final component of biodiversity is the richness of genes within species. Within each species or populations of a species there is variation of genes that keeps the species healthy. It is important to maintain several populations of every species, and to understand how genes flow between those populations to ensure that the richness of genes is maintained. Taxonomists are working to map the genetics of many species groups within the Coral Triangle to understand how organisms are linked via ocean currents, and where the boundaries of the Coral Triangle may lie.

Left: Coral reefs can grow to enormous sizes in clear water under the right conditions.

Above: Spinner Dolphins (*Stenella longirostris*) are a pantropical species of marine mammal that are well known for their acrobatic aerial displays.

EARLY EXPLORATION

At the time when WWF was mapping global ecoregions, species richness in the seas still presented particular challenges not found on land. Marine species can be sampled only by fishing or direct observation underwater. By the end of the 1990s, scientists estimated that less than 0.1 per cent of the volume of the oceans had been sampled (O'Dor, Miloslavich & Yarincik, 2010).

Early sampling was confined to what was caught through fishing techniques, and direct observation was only really possible after SCUBA was invented in 1943 (Ecott, 2002). Even with the miracle of SCUBA, scientists could only spend a few hours a day observing or collecting underwater, while terrestrial biologists can tromp through the forests for days on end. This presents a paradox of marine biology – it is acknowledged that it is harder for a casual observer to find animals in the rainforest than on a coral reef. However, first-time snorkellers on a coral reef are amazed to see so many fish and corals (G. Allen & Steene, 2002). So while animals are readily apparent on a coral reef, studying them is particularly difficult.

In the 1850s the great explorer of the Coral Triangle's islands, Alfred Russel Wallace, sailed into the natural harbour of Ambon and reported (Wallace, 1869) that the

> clearness of the water afforded me one of the most astonishing and beautiful sights I have ever beheld. The bottom was absolutely hidden by a continuous series of corals, sponges, actinias, and other marine productions, of magnificent dimensions, varied forms, and brilliant colours. The depth varied from about twenty to fifty feet, and the bottom was very uneven, rocks and chasms and little hills and valleys, offering a variety of stations for the growth of these animal forests. In and out among them, moved numbers of blue and red and yellow fishes, spotted and banded and striped in the most striking manner, while great orange or rosy transparent medusae floated along near the surface. It was a sight to gaze at for hours, and no description can do justice to its surpassing beauty and interest.

For once, the reality exceeded the most glowing accounts I had ever read of the wonders of a coral sea. There is perhaps no spot in the world richer in marine productions, corals, shells and fishes, than the harbour of Amboyna.

Wallace was not the only person to notice the richness of Indonesia's seas. Early Dutch naturalists such as Pieter Bleeker, an army officer stationed in the Dutch East Indies, collected marine samples from around the archipelago, and documented fish and corals throughout Indonesia from the mid-1800s (G. R. Allen & Adrim, 2003).

A similar interest in marine collection did not start in the Philippines until much later. After one particularly extensive exploration voyage, American scientist James Dana reported in 1875 that the East Indies and the Philippines were devoid of extensive coral-reef systems, and speculated that the presence of volcanoes may hinder development in the area. It was not until the mid-20th century that the area started to gain recognition as a global centre of marine biodiversity (Hoeksema, 2007).

Until the 1950s one of the planet's three greatest centres of biodiversity remained relatively hidden from human perception. The Amazon forest is the best known of these centres, and second to it are the forests and rivers of the Congo Basin. The third great centre of biodiversity – the Coral Triangle – is defined not by physical boundaries, but by the species richness found in the region. As such the boundaries are indistinct and change depending on how species are counted, how much effort is put into this and what the area is that scientists use to count species (Hoeksema, 2007).

Opposite: The largest of the Giant Clams (*Tridacna gigas*) is collected for its meat and shell and is listed as Vulnerable on the IUCN Red List of Threatened Species. It may already be extinct in Fiji and New Caledonia and is now rare throughout the Coral Triangle.

Table 1: Areas covered by the world's greatest biodiversity centres						
	Amazon	Congo	Borneo	New Guinea	Caribbean	Coral Triangle
Area (1,000s sq km)	5,500	4,014	743	786	2,754	5,700
Countries	8	9	3	2	27[1]	6[2]

[1] Overseas territories of the USA and Europe not counted individually.
[2] Based on the delineation of Veron et al., 2009. Larger definitions can include Brunei Darussalam and Singapore.

The TERM 'CORAL TRIANGLE'

ONE of the first mentions of a centre of diversity in the region came in 1953, in Sven Ekman's English translation of *Zoogeography of the Seas*. This landmark work combined and synthesized data from hundreds of other expeditions, and concluded that the 'Indo-West Pacific', an area stretching from the east coast of Africa to the centre of the Pacific Ocean, held the greatest wealth of marine life.

Subsequent to Ekman's report more and more scientists began mapping marine species occurrences, and the area around the

islands between Asia and Australia kept showing up as the highest in the world. Several scientists drew various shapes around the area, and one of the most common was a triangle that encompassed the Philippines, Indonesia and Papua New Guinea. All of the triangles (and other shapes) varied from each other, and usually the edges were more abstract than a true biogeographic demarcation (Hoeksema, 2007).

The exact origin of the term 'Coral Triangle' is unclear, but the first use in scientific literature came in 1994 in an early attempt to map coral reefs of the world using computer-aided mapping techniques (McAllister et al., in Hoeksema, 2007). The usage of the term grew with time. In the late 1990s WWF started to work on two 'ecoregion conservation' programmes in the Sulu Sulawesi Marine Ecoregion (Indonesia, Malaysia and the Philippines) and Bismarck Solomon Seas Ecoregion (Indonesia, Papua New Guinea and the Solomon Islands). Those two programmes expanded conservation efforts to include the scale of ecological processes and multinational efforts in the marine realm.

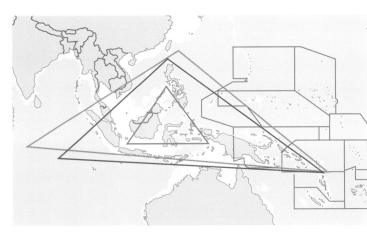

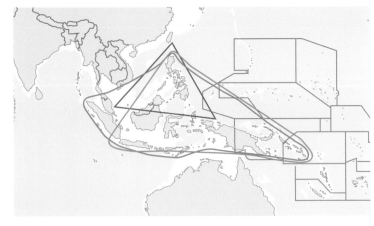

Above: Various early delineations of the Coral Triange region.

At around the same time Conservation International started a series of rapid assessments of the marine environment in Indonesia, the Philippines, Papua New Guinea and the Solomon Islands. In its early reports it mentioned the Coral Triangle, but included Japan and Australia in its definition (Alonso, Deichmann, Mckenna, Naskrecki & Richards, 2011).

The term Coral Triangle was formalized in 2009 when the heads of state of Indonesia, Malaysia, Papua New Guinea, the Philippines, the Solomon Islands and Timor Leste signed an agreement at the World Ocean's Conference in Manado, Indonesia. The agreement, the Coral Triangle Initiative on Coral Reefs, Fisheries and Food

Security, solidified the Veron et al (2009) definition of the scientific boundaries of the Coral Triangle, while acknowledging that as a management area the Coral Triangle must encompass the claimed waters of the member countries (see also page 33).

Above: Si Amil Island, on Malaysia's easternmost reef, may soon form part of a massive marine park.

Opposite: Kofiau Island, in Indonesia's Raja Ampat, harbours some of the highest marine biodiversity in the world.

The AREA'S RICHNESS

WHILE there is little doubt that the Coral Triangle is the richest marine environment on the planet, the reasons for the richness are hotly debated. Is it because the richest taxonomic groups originated in the Coral Triangle and dispersed to the rest of the world? Or is it because of the overlap of flora and fauna from the West Pacific Ocean and Indian Ocean? As it turns out, the only thing that is clear is that the reasons for the area's richness are complex and no single model explains it all.

Some of the many factors that influence the diversity of the Coral Triangle are the geological history of the region, including plate tectonics and sea-level fluctuations; how species disperse and the factors that facilitate or inhibit dispersal; general biogeographic patterns and evolutionary forces.

The tropics are generally more species rich than temperate and polar areas particularly because of the constant sunlight regime and weather stability. Without a winter period, organisms can flourish year round and put more energy into specialization than into preparing for long periods with reduced sunlight. This is as true in the marine realm as it is in the forests, where light and relatively constant warm water temperatures persist throughout the year. However, coastal tropical waters are relatively nutrient poor.

The annual changes in water temperatures of the temperate and polar seas produce mixing when the surface waters cool and sink to the bottom. The displaced bottom waters, rich with dead plankton that has sank to the depths, are forced to the surface and result in huge explosions of zooplankton and fish populations. Such mixing does not happen in the tropics because the surface waters remain warm year round. The richness here is centred on the coral reefs that survive by building intricate relationships between organisms, resulting in habitats with many niches of incredible biodiversity surrounded by virtual deserts of nutrient-poor ocean.

The wide variation in habitats in the Coral Triangle also helps to explain the diversity. With so many islands, there is ample area for coral-reef growth. Some of the islands border deep-sea basins, and some border shallow continental shelves. At a local scale, large areas of coral reef like Malaysia's Semporna Archipelago and the Indonesian Spermonde Archipelago have a rich mix of reef types, with some exposed to high-energy areas facing open seas and others in sheltered bays. This leads to different species occupying these different habitats and increases the richness of the Coral Triangle.

The Coral Triangle lies at the intersection of the Indian and Pacific Oceans. It may be the richest marine environment in the world simply because of the overlap of so many different marine ecoregions.

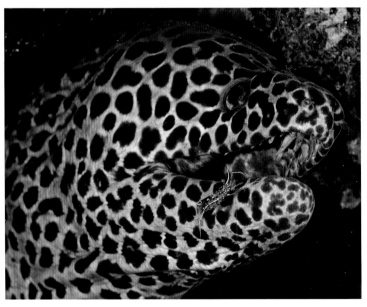

Above: One of the two largest moray eels in the Coral Triangle, the Honeycomb Moray (*Gymnothorax favagineus*) can grow up to 3 m (10 ft).

Top: The Thornback Cowfish (*Lactoria fornasini*) may be one of the strangest looking fish on Coral Triangle reefs.

Opposite: The lagoon of Tun Sakaran Marine Park provides habitat different from reefs exposed to strong waves and currents facing the Sulawesi Sea.

Due to ocean circulation patterns and the rotation of the Earth, the western Pacific Ocean is slightly higher than the eastern Indian Ocean and there is a strong current, the Indonesian Through-flow, which diverts Pacific waters to the Indian Ocean. Currents moving out of the Coral Triangle region to the north and south bring larvae into cooler temperate waters along the coast of Australia and north to Japan. The cooler environments are less suitable for corals and reefs. Thus, coral and fish larvae are brought to the Coral Triangle from the Pacific Ocean, but when currents leave the Coral Triangle any exported organisms are unlikely to survive.

The relatively recent history of ice-age related sea-level changes is thought to have contributed to the richness. As sea levels dropped by more than 100 m (328 ft) circulation patterns changed, deep basins were isolated, and many seabeds were exposed and the newly exposed reefs died. Within those isolated basins marine species may have evolved into new species. Rivers were draining larger continental areas and the outflow became a freshwater barrier to larvae migrating along the coast, further isolating organisms that could not disperse through the less saline waters. The large continental shelf areas of the Sunda and Arafura Seas were exposed.

As the glaciers melted and sea levels rose, the newly evolved species were free to mix around the Coral Triangle area and recolonize the previously exposed land – a process that is ongoing.

Above: The sea level 17,000 years ago was approximately 120 m (400 ft) lower than it is now and the Sunda and Sahul Shelves isolated parts of the Coral Triangle perhaps leading to some of its richness.

Right: The Harlequin Hind (*Cephalopholis polleni*) is a rare grouper that only occupies oceanic islands and reefs and is rarely found shallower than 30 m (100 ft).

Below: Many marine species have a pelagic larval stage. This anemone (*Nemanthidae* spp.) will settle when it detects a suitable habitat.

Traditional evolutionary theory suggests that isolation of populations leads to the emergence of new species. However, it was long presumed that such isolation was uncommon in the seas because of ocean currents and the larval dispersal of many organisms. If that was true, then the Coral Triangle's many habitats could not have led to such high richness of species. Several theories are being developed to explain it.

Many marine species reproduce by producing microscopic larvae that move with ocean currents until they arrive at a suitable habitat and can begin to grow. This reproductive strategy, especially for sessile organisms like corals, resembles mass pollination among trees. Among corals, all of the animals emit millions of eggs and sperm into the sea on the same night across hundreds of kilometres of reef. By doing this all at once, they help to ensure the greatest chance of fertilization, and that a precious few of the fertilized eggs will escape predation. The fertilized eggs grow into larvae that were once thought to drift helplessly along the currents until they reached an age, after several hours or months, when they transformed and hopefully settled into a suitable juvenile habitat. If the larvae were caught in a strong current, they could be taken far away to bring new genetic material to a distant area. However, if the current had to pass a cold upwelling or the freshwater plume of a large river, the connectivity could be broken. Such barriers could isolate populations and lead to speciation.

There is, however, some debate about the role that the larvae play in their own distribution. Scientists are now hypothesizing that the larvae are not helpless drifters, but can influence where the currents take them (Almany et al., 2013). A recent study from Papua New Guinea's Manus Island showed that 25 per cent of juvenile groupers found in a small protected area came from parents that had spawned in the same area. Another series of studies examined the genetic similarities of mantis shrimps in parts of the Coral Triangle (Barber, Palumbi, Erdmann & Moosa, 2000). The scientists sampled the mantis shrimps in areas where the fast-moving Indonesian Through-flow current would be expected to link populations across more than 600 km (373 miles) based on their 4–6-week larval stage. Instead, they were surprised to find distinct genetic differences over much smaller distances. This suggested that there were some biogeographic barriers that stopped populations from mixing thoroughly. Such studies show that the previously held notion that marine populations were all connected over long distances may not be entirely correct and that there are barriers to mixing, even when ocean currents seem to link distant populations.

Above: Peacock Mantis Shrimps (*Odontodactylus scyllarus*) have one of the fastest attacks of any animal with their powerful front legs.

Top: Red Coral Groupers are highly prized in the live reef-food fish trade for their bright red colour and flaky flesh. Some consumers claim that they can tell the difference between a fish from the Philippines and one from Australia because of differences in the skin thickness.

So, while there is evidence that populations of marine organisms in the Coral Triangle may be more isolated than previously thought and this may have led to the extreme richness, there is a contrasting hypothesis that the flow of larvae and genes is exactly what has led to such richness. This theory, known as 'reticulate evolution', at first glance seems to fly in the face of traditional models of evolution.

Reticulate evolution dispenses with many of the fundamentals of older theories of evolution, and the notion of a species as the building block of taxonomy is disputed. Instead, genetic diversity is considered to be along a continuum in both space and time, rather than being divided into distinct units that cannot interbreed. According to the theory, organisms in one area may change their genetic code slightly, then eventually recombine with a similar organism in a different place at a different time. Thus the concept of the 'tree of life' is exchanged with that of a 'web of life'. While some evidence for this has been found among some marine taxa, in the Coral Triangle it is proposed as an explanation for the richness of corals; in this case it is exactly the currents and the mixing of the waters of the Coral Triangle that move genetic material around and allow new corals to form and mix and form again (Arnold & Fogarty, 2009; Science, 2014; Veron, Devantier, Turak & Green, 2009).

PEOPLE *in the* CORAL TRIANGLE

THE Coral Triangle's riches are not only in the realm of biodiversity. Some of the world's most diverse human communities live along its shores and depend upon it for their livelihoods and sustenance. Nowhere else in the world do so many people depend on such high biodiversity and live among it in such concentrations. There are more than 120 million people living across the Coral Triangle region, with a vast array of cultures, languages and lifestyles. Manila and Jakarta are huge megacities with millions of inhabitants. Other communities across the region inhabit tiny islands without electricity, access to a consistent freshwater supply or schools. There are still communities of sea nomads that are born, live and die on small boats. They once roamed vast areas of the Coral Triangle, but are now struggling with the concept of national borders and laws that restrict access to their ancestral fishing grounds. Papua New Guinea is famous for its 800 languages and cultural diversity to match. Coastal communities in Papua New Guinea and the Solomon Islands still maintain close associations with their traditional fishing grounds and rituals, but in many areas those traditions are quickly eroding. Religion plays an important role in almost every Coral Triangle community. Christianity, Islam, Buddhism and Hinduism are all found along the region's shores. These religions are frequently mixed with elements of earlier beliefs that have close associations with the sea. The seas of the Coral Triangle have long sustained its diverse cultures; and in many areas, local traditions are being revived in attempts to conserve the dwindling resources and save the Coral Triangle, along with its cultures.

Left: In Papua New Guinea, coastal communities own reefs just as they own land, and fishing is regulated among community members.

Below: Squid caught overnight in Indonesia's Suva Sea National Marine Park are salted and dried for sale to traders who take them to Jakarta and Singapore.

Opposite: In many parts of the Coral Triangle communities such as this one on Boheyan Island, Semporna, live in constant contact with the sea.

Table 2: Languages of the Coral Triangle

	Indonesia	Malaysia	Papua New Guinea	The Philippines	Solomon Islands	Timor Leste
Living	706	138	836	181	71	19
Extinct	13	2	12	4	4	1
Total	719	140	848	185	75	20

THREATS *to the* CORAL TRIANGLE

UNFORTUNATELY, the riches of the Coral Triangle are under threat. A series of landmark studies modelled threats to coral reefs around the world in 1998, with a Coral Triangle specific follow-up in 2013. The 2013 study found that the coral reefs of the Coral Triangle are under much higher threat than the average reef around the world. Some 85 per cent of reefs in the Coral Triangle are locally threatened, with 45 per cent at high or very high levels of threats. By 2030 the number of reefs in the high to very high threat categories is expected to rise to 80 per cent. When global threats caused by climate change are included in the analysis, the total of threatened reefs climbs to 90 per cent.

Threats to the resources of the Coral Triangle are entirely a manifestation of human activity. People behave in ways that put too much pressure on the resources, and reduce their ability to play the roles that they have evolved to play in the ecosystem. In extreme cases species are driven to extinction and the ecosystem stops functioning. Conservation of biodiversity and natural ecosystems requires that people at all levels of society change their behaviours to reduce the impacts on the planet's resources. This is the role of resource-management agencies, conservation groups, and – increasingly – the private sector and civil society.

In the Coral Triangle the threats can be broadly grouped into overfishing, destructive fishing and climate-change impacts, as well as over-development and pollution (marine based and land based). In order to preserve the biodiversity, organisms and habitats, behaviours that result in these threats must be changed.

OVERFISHING

This is a global problem. Current fishing practices are one of the biggest threats to the seas. As recently as 100 years ago most people thought that the seas were too immense to be over-exploited. We now know differently. Too many fishing boats employing modern gear are targeting too few fish. They started by catching the biggest and most desirable fish, and as these became increasingly rare, switched to smaller and smaller fish. Where we once consumed top predators, we are working our way down the food chain. Some scientists predict a day when we will be eating mostly plankton and jellyfish. In addition to simply fishing too much, many fishing practices are inherently destructive and wasteful (see opposite).

As many as 85 per cent of the world's fisheries are at maximum capacity, overfished or recovering from overfishing (FAO, 2010). Not only are we fishing too many fish; we are also altering the nature of ecosystems by selectively removing the top predators and taking fish lower and lower down the food chain (Pauly, Christensen & Dalsgaard, 1998). In the case of the Coral Triangle, fish is a staple of the people living in the area. Those living on small islands, with no extra land on which to cultivate crops or graze livestock, have no choice but to turn to the sea for the majority of their protein. Meanwhile in the Southeast Asian megacities, people rely on fish protein as a cheap source of nutrition.

In the Coral Triangle overfishing is manifested on many levels. Fish-resource surveys have shown that the number and size of fish targeted by commercial trawlers in Malaysia, the Philippines and Thailand have declined by 90 per cent in most areas since the 1960s. Coral reefs, which support many of the small-scale and subsistence fisheries, are showing similar declines in fish biomass.

Proximity to human populations tends to be bad for marine resources. Coral reefs, mangroves and fish populations closest to big human settlements are often the most degraded. Some 30 per cent

of the residents of the Coral Triangle, nearly 114 million people, live within 30 km (19 miles) of a coral reef. Nearly every reef in the Philippines, Malaysia and Timor Leste is thought to be threatened by overfishing (Burke et al., 2013). Only some reefs in distant parts of Indonesia, Papua New Guinea and the Solomon Islands are remote enough to not be severely threatened by overfishing.

The Philippines and Indonesia have some of the world's most highly populated small islands, which depend almost entirely on the resources of the sea. With no other industry from which to make a living, and no food stores to shop in (even if they had money), the people depend on daily fish catches to feed their families and earn enough money for fuel for the next fishing trip. This dependence, coupled with rapid population growth, has led to the deterioration of many of the Coral Triangle's reefs, mangroves and other marine resources. In the eastern Coral Triangle the human populations are smaller but the countries are generally poorer, and the people just as dependent on the marine resources as in the west of the area.

The western Coral Triangle (the Philippines, Malaysia and western Indonesia) is characterized by relatively large and dense human populations. The island of Java is the most heavily populated island on Earth. Some of the small islands of the Philippines have population densities similar to Java's, but without the land resources and with only the sea to sustain them. Indonesia is the fourth most populous country, and the Philippines is the world's twelfth. Malaysia has a much smaller population than its larger neighbours, and east Malaysia's states of Sabah and Sarawak (on Borneo) are Malaysia's least densely populated. The megacities of Manila, Jakarta and Kuala Lumpur host millions of people who have a cultural tradition of living off the sea and depending on seafood.

Conversely, the eastern Coral Triangle (the Solomon Islands, Papua New Guinea, Timor Leste and eastern Indonesia) is mostly characterized by much smaller human impacts, although locally such impacts can be as great or greater than in the western part. However, these are the poorest countries in the Coral Triangle and have the lowest Human Development Index ranking in the region (hdr.undp.org/en/countries). Timor Leste only emerged from 30 years of conflict and occupation in 1999, and is still striving to recover and develop. In these poor countries a large portion of the population depends directly on the sea for food and livelihoods.

DESTRUCTIVE FISHING

Destructive fishing runs a wide gamut of definitions. From overly selective fisheries targeting only large individuals (spearfishing) to completely unselective fisheries that also wipe out huge swathes of habitat (bottom trawling, blast fishing), destructive fishing is often a wasteful practice that can be relatively easy to eliminate with the right incentives.

Bottom trawling, the practice of dragging a net along the seabed – often with a chain at the bottom to scare organisms out of the mud – is akin to clear-cutting a forest. Any rocks, corals, sponges and other habitats in the path of the trawl are annihilated when the chain sweeps through them. It has been estimated that of the world's continental shelf equivalent up to three times the size of Brazil is trawled every year.

Blast fishing, the practice of using explosives in the water to kill or stun fish, is an extremely destructive fishing practice employed extensively in Indonesia, Malaysia and the Philippines, but less so in other areas. Introduced after the Second World War using unexploded ordinance, the practice has continued today with fishermen building their own bombs from chemical fertilizers and soda bottles. The bombs usually target schools of fish on coral reefs, but often end up destroying the reefs themselves. In many areas entire reefs have been converted to fields of rubble that would take hundreds of years to recover.

On a smaller scale many fishermen use sodium cyanide to stun fish, then collect them alive for sale as aquarium specimens or as live 'fresh' fish for east Asian restaurants. The cyanide often kills the corals and other organisms the fish were hiding among, and the fishermen break apart the reef when the stunned fish retreat into coral crevices.

Above: Using explosives to catch fish, a practice still common in many parts of the Coral Triangle, can destroy large areas of fragile reefs.

Opposite: This fishing net in Timor Leste's Nino Konis Santana National Park has entangled corals and trapped fish long after it was lost or discarded by fishermen on a boat.

Above: A Green Sea Turtle takes refuge in a gigantic barrel sponge at Sipadan Island.

HALTING *the* DESTRUCTION

DESPITE the problems, there is hope for the Coral Triangle. Because the biodiversity is not just a remote and abstract concept far away from human eyes, it is real to many people and that gives it a chance. Many local communities understand that they must maintain ecosystems for their own future security. The growing tourism industry, for diving, beach vacations, surfing and cultural tourism, is beginning to recognize the value of healthy ecosystems. Governments of the region have acknowledged the need to protect this important area. In 2009 the heads of state of all six Coral Triangle countries signed an agreement to work together to protect the coral reefs, fisheries and food security together (see box below).

The Coral Triangle Initiative for Coral Reefs, Fisheries and Food Security

In 2009 the leaders of six countries came together at the World Ocean Summit in Manado, Indonesia and signed the Regional Plan of Action for the Coral Triangle Initiative on Coral Reefs, Fisheries and Food Security (CTI-CFF). That action launched one of the largest marine biodiversity conservation initiatives in the world.

The concept for a Coral Triangle agreement between the countries of the region was originally proposed by Indonesia's President Susilo Bambang Yudhoyono in 2006. President Yudhoyono then won support for his suggestion from all 21 heads of government at the 2007 Asia Pacific Economic Cooperation meeting. Over the next two years ministers and officials from all six Coral Triangle countries, Indonesia, Malaysia, Papua New Guinea, the Philippines, the Solomon Islands and Timor Leste, supported by partners from multilateral and bilateral aid agencies, environmental NGOs and private sector partners, drafted a regional agreement that would become the Regional Plan of Action.

At the highest levels of government, the six countries agreed on several key principles for cooperative management of the Coral Triangle's marine resources, and drafted five broad goals to be achieved by 2020. The principles were that the CTI should:

1: Support people-centered biodiversity conservation, sustainable development, poverty reduction and equitable benefit sharing.

2: Be based on solid science.

3: Be centred on quantitative goals and timetables adopted by governments at the highest political levels.

4: Use existing and future forums to promote implementation.

5: Be aligned with international and regional commitments.

6: Recognize the trans-boundary nature of some important marine natural resources.

7: Emphasize priority geographies.

8: Be inclusive and engage multiple stakeholders.

9: Recognize the uniqueness, fragility and vulnerability of island ecosystems.

Above: By-catch is one of the many issues to be tackled by the Coral Triangle Initiative. Coupled with overfishing and destructive fishing, unsustainable fishing is one of the biggest threats.

In the Regional Plan of Action they set five goals that cover:

1. Conservation on a large, seascape level.

2. Employing an ecosystem approach to fisheries management.

3. Introducing more marine protected areas and managing existing ones better.

4. Adapting to climate change.

5. Addressing issues surrounding threatened species.

The five goals are bolstered by 10 targets detailing each of the overarching goals.

Before the establishment of the CTI-CFF, other governmental and NGO programmes and projects addressed issues at national and local levels, with a few projects spanning large areas. With such high biodiversity, the region has been a global priority for conservation for decades. Environmental NGOs operate marine-conservation projects in all of the Coral Triangle countries. A host of smaller, local conservation organizations has sprung up in each country to further the efforts of conservation. Early projects focused largely on establishing marine protected areas and on endangered species, particularly marine turtles.

MARINE PROTECTED AREAS

These are one of the main tools for marine conservation. A marine protected area can be any area of the sea or coast where some activities are restricted. There is a universe of definitions and types of marine protected area in the Coral Triangle. Some are huge areas that exclude all fishing. Others are tiny corners of an island protected by a local community living nearby for cultural or traditional reasons. Others still are protected areas that use zoning to allow different uses in different areas, and some regulate according to the season.

Some of the region's most famous marine parks were established through cooperation between NGOs and national governments. However, in the early days the establishment of national parks often entailed excluding people from the area. As more protected areas were declared it became harder and harder to remove local residents, often poor fishermen dependent on the reefs. In the 1990s the paradigm changed and protected areas started to become friendlier to local populations by allowing them access to some reefs.

Whatever the exact definition of a marine protected area, it is known that a much smaller proportion of the oceans is protected than land. In 2006 the eighth meeting of the Convention on Biological Diversity set a target that 10 per cent of the world's oceans should be protected by 2010. As of 2008 only 0.65 per cent of the oceans had any protection, and a miniscule 0.08 per cent was totally protected from fishing (Wood, Fish, Laughren & Pauly, 2008). However, there is clear evidence that when fishing pressure is reduced, or eliminated, fish populations can quickly rebound. Bigger fish produce more eggs at an exponential scale. So if a protected area allows some fish to grow large, those fish can send eggs and larvae to other reefs nearby and further away, where they can be caught later. If these protected areas are designed within a network where they are connected by ocean currents, they can support biodiversity and enhance fisheries.

The Coral Triangle countries are making great strides in establishing more protected areas. However, it is widely acknowledged that existing areas often suffer from a lack of management. Human resources, funds, local support and political will are all needed to ensure that a protected area is well managed. The management can be done by a government agency, a local community or even a private company. In many cases there is no management on the ground and the areas become just 'paper parks' – existing on paper but with nothing happening on the ground other than the business-as-usual activities that threatened them in the first place.

Above: Sea fans are soft corals that rely on filtering plankton from the water column. They frequently grow out from a reef, perpendicular to prevailing currents.

Table 3: Summary of the Coral Triangle's (CT) marine protected areas (MPAs)

CT country	Total number of MPAs	Number of MPAs with known boundaries	Total area (sq km) for known boundaries	Percentage of EEZ[1]	Percentage of territorial waters (12 nautical miles)
Indonesia	108	83	157,841	2.7	13.1
Malaysia	51	50	15,661	3.5	12.7
Papua New Guinea	59	35	4,558	0.2	1.3
Philippines	1,653	248	20,940	1.1	4.2
Solomon Islands	100	82	1325	0.1	0.9
Timor-Leste	1	1	556	1.3	3.4
Region	1,972	599	200,881	1.6	9.4

Coral Triangle Initiative on Coral Reefs, Fisheries and Food Security (CTI-CFF), 2013.
[1]Exclusive Economic Zone (EEZ): prescribed sea zone usually 200 nautical miles from the coast over which a state has special rights.

PROTECTING SPECIES

Protecting endangered species in the Coral Triangle is a particular challenge because many of them migrate between countries. Marine turtles, Dugongs (*Dugong dugon*), whales and dolphins are protected in most of the Coral Triangle countries, but there are gaps in the protection. In Malaysia turtles are fully protected in some states, but in others it is still legal to openly buy and sell turtle eggs. In parts of Indonesia marine turtles are still hunted for their meat, and poachers from China and Vietnam are regularly caught in Coral Triangle waters with boatloads of living and dead endangered turtles. However, the efforts of the Philippines and Malaysia to protected the Turtle Islands and declare them as Southeast Asia's first transboundary marine protected area went a long way towards protecting two species.

Protecting endangered species and establishing parks are two of the best tools for conservation, but they are in danger of becoming jewels in a pile of refuse if the seas around them continue to deteriorate. Protected areas will almost certainly fail if nearby factories and rivers continue to spew pollution into the sea near them, and if uncontrolled fisheries suck up all the fish and destroy the ecosystems in the unprotected parts of the sea.

Below: Hawksbill Turtles (*Eretmochelys imbricata*), like all marine turtles, must surface occasionally to breathe, but can remain submerged for several minutes when active or for several hours when resting.

Above: Pygmy Blue Whales (*Balaenoptera musculus brevicauda*) are a subspecies of the Blue Whale and can reach 24 m (78 ft) in length. They are part of an initiative among Pacific Island nations to further protect whales.

Right: The Spinner Dolphin is a coastal species that feeds on many small pelagic fish targeted by purse-seines and trawls. It is often caught as by-catch.

Opposite: Grazing by Dugongs is an important ecological process in seagrass beds. Organisms have evolved to cope with the grazing and to take advantage of the disturbances it causes. As Dugong populations dwindle, the impacts on seagrasses may be large.

SUSTAINABLE FISHING

Changing the way in which fisheries are managed is one of the key factors in saving the Coral Triangle. All six countries have agreed to change their approach to managing fisheries and adopt a stance that considers not only the fish, but also the ecosystem that they live in and the people who depend on them for a living. This system, often called an 'ecosystem approach to fisheries management', remains a somewhat nebulous concept but an important one. The critical points are that fisheries managers understand and recognize that fish production requires a clean and healthy ecosystem, and they need tools to help them achieve both.

While governments and NGOs have long taken on the role of managing and conserving the marine environment of the Coral Triangle, the private sector and general public are playing increasingly large roles, particularly in the fisheries and aquaculture sectors. This follows from movements in Western countries where consumers are demanding seafood products that are sourced from sustainable fisheries. The Marine Stewardship Council has been certifying wild-caught fisheries since 1997. Its counterpart for cultured fish, the Aquaculture Stewardship Council, has only recently been formed. Both entities are still struggling to build awareness in the Coral Triangle. Awareness of sustainable fisheries is rising among consumers in urban areas through campaigns led by conservation NGOs. On a smaller scale, local communities on small islands are being given tools to manage their local fisheries and ecosystems in order to ensure their food security and income.

SUSTAINABLE TOURISM

A key component of the solutions to the Coral Triangle's threats is tourism. It is a double-edged sword. Visitors often want to spend time on pristine beaches and remote islands, and snorkel or SCUBA dive on coral reefs. Tourism can bring alternative income to small island communities, and provide jobs for fishermen and their families. However, it often brings poorly planned development and pollution. Too many tourists in one area can stress a coral reef or population of animals. Tourism can also bring issues of equity into the picture. Can poor fishing communities that are entirely reliant on access to coral reefs be excluded from the leisure activities of relatively wealthy tourists?

RESPONSES TO CLIMATE CHANGE

It is often difficult to observe the effects of climate change on the reefs and other habitats of the Coral Triangle. The immediate and local threats and impacts of overuse are so pervasive and acute that the insidious and gradual effects of a changing climate are difficult to isolate and observe. However, many scientists and conservationists are taking a long-term view to identify strategies to help coral reefs adapt to a changing climate. Reefs are naturally quite resilient, but they need to be healthy to respond to the changing environment. Not every reef responds to climate stressors in the same way. Reefs that are healthy, connected via currents to other reefs and already adapted to high stresses show the greatest ability to respond to climate stresses. By identifying and protecting these key reefs, it is hoped that all reefs will be better able to withstand the current changes to the planet's climate systems.

Left: To be considered sustainable, tourism must meet environmental and social goals. Poor communities need to benefit from tourism income.

Table 4: Direct contribution of tourism to Coral Triangle economies in 2012						
	Indonesia	Malaysia	Papua New Guinea	The Philippines	Solomon Islands	Timor Leste
Per cent of GDP	3	7	1.3	2	5.2	No data
Direct income (US $b)	26.2	21.2	0.2	5.1	0.05	No data
World Travel and Tourism Council, 2013.						

Climate Change and the Coral Triangle Initiative

Our climate is changing. With existing levels of greenhouse gases, we are already committed to certain changes that could bring the Coral Triangle's resources close to complete destruction. Any further increases in greenhouse gases will only exacerbate the situation.

Several direct impacts are already being recorded and predicted to get worse, including more frequent coral bleaching and weakened coral skeletons from ocean acidification. Natural sex ratios of turtles will be altered. Indirect impacts are coming from changes in rainfall and storm patterns.

Increased atmospheric temperatures are raising sea temperatures. Corals live within narrow temperature ranges and when the seas exceed the coral's maximum tolerable temperature they expel the critical algae (see page 42) from their cells and begin to starve. If the temperatures are not quickly reduced, the corals die. Since it is the algae that give the corals their colour, the process of corals turning white as they expel algae is referred to as 'coral bleaching'.

The oceans naturally absorb a portion of the increased atmospheric carbon dioxide. The resulting chemical reactions reduce the water's pH as carbonic acid is formed. This inhibits the ability of organisms to efficiently produce calcium carbonate – a critical component of building shells and coral skeletons in the Coral Triangle.

The sex of turtle hatchlings is determined by the temperature of their nests. Slightly warmer temperatures result in more females. As the atmosphere and seas heat up, the impact on imbalanced turtle populations may further threaten their survival.

The changing climate will also change rainfall patterns across the Coral Triangle, with some places experiencing higher rainfalls and other areas experiencing prolonged drought. Freshwater inputs help define where corals can grow and many reefs may be unable to survive under this new regime. The altered atmosphere also changes the frequency and strength of monsoons and storms, which will cause beaches to erode or accrete, and islands to be lost or to grow beyond the edges of their fringing reefs. The complex currents that flow through the Coral Triangle, carrying eggs and larvae of many organsims to new homes, will also change. Rising sea levels will inundate shallow coastal ecosystems, particularly mangroves and seagrasses, vastly changing their distributions.

People living in close association with the coastal ecosystems of the Coral Triangle are particularly vulnerable to the impacts of climate change. In many cases they have no options for other livelihoods and no other place to go if their homes are lost to rising seas or eroding coastlines. The impacts on communities will be largely determined by their ability to adapt to new conditions.

The countries of the Coral Triangle are just beginning to respond to the looming threats of climate change. One of the most obvious responses is to reduce greenhouse gas emissions, but the Coral Triangle only emitted 2.2 per cent of the world's carbon dioxide in 2004 (Hoegh-Guldberg et al., 2009). Without drastic reductions in emissions from some of the world's biggest contributors, the Coral Triangle countries must prepare for worst-case scenarios.

Marine ecosystems tend to be naturally resilient to threats. They are intimately linked via currents and the movements of organisms. If one area is degraded, it can often recover quickly if the local threat is removed. A key strategy for coping with climate change is to promote ecosystem resilience by ensuring the stability of ecosystems to better respond to climate change impacts.

Goal 4 of the CTI-CFF is to achieve climate change adaptation measures (see page 33). The early action plan has the twin objectives of maintaining biodiversity and ecosystem services that are important for 'income, livelihoods and food security' of coastal communities, and to help diversify the livelihood options of those coastal communities. The plan should help both the ecosystems and the communities to become resilient to the impacts of a changing climate. To achieve this the Coral Triangle countries will need to intensify conservation efforts already in place while implementing the action plans for climate adaptation. Existing strategies to reduce local threats like habitat destruction, overfishing and pollution will strengthen the ability of habitats and organisms to adapt to changing climatic conditions.

It is important to know which ecosystems and which communities are most vulnerable to climate change. To achieve this involves collecting more information on ecosystems and habitats to prioritize those most at risk. Identifying areas that are most resistant to the impacts of climate change is a key task. For instance, some coral reefs seem to be less prone to bleaching perhaps because they are close to sources of deeper, cool water, or are buffeted by strong currents that do not allow hot water to accumulate. There are also many steps to promote social resilience. Communities that rely on only one source of income or that are overly dependent on a vulnerable habitat, like a mangrove forest that may be flooded, need help to diversify their livelihoods and to prepare for the changes that are coming.

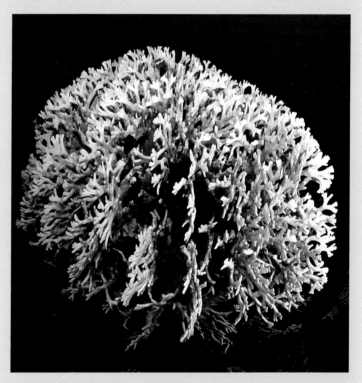

Above: *The white skeleton of coral is visible when it looses its zooxanthellae as a result of stress, including that caused by extended elevated temperatures. The coral appears bleached and can die if the situation does not return to normal quickly.*

2
RICH HABITATS *of* *the* CORAL TRIANGLE

The Coral Triangle's extreme species richness is due in part to the wide variety and sheer acreage of habitats available for colonization, specialization and evolution. Three habitats are usually considered the 'big three' for conservation because of their high productivity, ecological value and superlative biodiversity. These are coral reefs, seagrass beds and mangroves. Other important habitats include beaches, shallow mudflats, the open seas, deep trenches, migratory passages between islands and seamounts.

Left: Deep embayments, such as this one in Indonesia, can be home to a very different array of biodiversity than an open ocean reef.

CORAL REEFS

A VISIT to a healthy coral reef can be a complete overload to the senses. There is action everywhere. Fish are the most obvious inhabitants and are everywhere you look – swimming, resting, feeding on plankton, building homes and waiting prone on the bottom for unsuspecting prey to swim too close. Beyond the fish are the infinite forms of coral, all packed in with each other and competing for space and light, and the hidden universe of ridiculously colourful tiny creatures or impossibly camouflaged ones that need a patient and well-practised eye to spot.

Coral reefs are biogenic geological features – they are stones made by living organisms – and can take tens of thousands of years to form into the big structures that we are most familiar with. Corals are relatively simple, tiny organisms related to jellyfish and sea anemones, and can be stony or soft. Stony corals are the ones that build reefs by cementing their calcium carbonate skeletons on top of those of their ancestors over long periods of time.

Most coral reefs, as opposed to deep-sea coral communities, are found in the tropics. Some may occur outside the tropics where warm equatorial currents wash up coastlines and extend the range of corals a bit further. Corals are extremely sensitive to their environment. They need clear, warm waters to grow to their maximum potential and richness. If water temperatures rise or fall by just a few degrees outside a narrow band, corals stop feeding and can die in a few weeks if the situation does not quickly revert back to normal.

One of the key characteristics of a coral reef is the relationship between the coral polyp and the microscopic algae that live within its tissues. The algae – called zooxanthellae – photosynthesize and produce sugars that help feed the corals. In turn, the corals give the algae a home and constitute a means of defence. This is the secret of how corals can survive in what is otherwise a nutrient desert, and what allows the magnificent diversity of the reefs to form.

HOW REEFS DEVELOP

Reefs are built primarily on the limestone secreted by each coral polyp living among thousands of others in colonies. The colonies grow as the coral polyps reproduce by budding, when an adult polyp splits into two. This process produces the intricate and varied coral forms that we see on reefs today. The shape of the coral colony is defined by the species of coral, and also by its environment. Delicate branching corals or plate corals often grow in relatively deep water, where waves and water movements are weaker or less severe than in more shallow water. More robust and stronger coral forms are found closer to the surface and can tolerate constant pounding by waves. Large brain corals are the most robust. However, it is not just the corals that build reefs. An important component is the coralline algae that bind a reef together – especially when fragments break off from a coral colony. Coralline algae are red algae that secrete a hard calcerous material in their cell walls. They can be seen on reefs as pink or grey mats between coral colonies or on dead corals. Without the coralline algae, broken corals would simply fall off the reef and never be cemented within the reef structure.

There are several types of reef formation, usually determined by the type of coastline, and within each reef there are distinct habitats defined by the wave and sunlight energy they receive. The most common theory for how a coral reef forms starts with a relatively shallow area – sunlight only penetrates seawater to about 40 m (130 ft) depth in enough concentration for reefs to form. If the conditions are right (in terms of temperature, sunlight and water quality), a coral larva may settle on a new habitat and start to grow. As it reproduces and as other larvae find the same area, the reef begins to grow towards the surface. Eventually several distinct zones are formed.

Above: Reefs destroyed by fish bombing, storms or fishing nets can take decades to begin to recover.

Opposite: Corals at the edge of the reef crest often bear the brunt of waves coming from the open sea and are more robust than corals at greater depths.

Table 1: Area of coral reef in the Coral Triangle

	Indonesia	Malaysia	Papua New Guinea	Philippines	Solomon Islands	Timor Leste
Square kilometres	51,020	3,600	13,840	25,060	5,750	800

Spalding et al., 2001.

From the depths, where the least light penetrates, the reef grows along the slope of the coast – called the reef slope. As the reef approaches the sea's surface it forms a crest, usually just at the level of the low tide. This crest is where the reef receives all the energy of waves that come from across the ocean. The corals that can survive at the reef crest are more robust than those at depth, which can be more delicate and fragile. Behind the reef crest, towards the beach, is the reef flat. This area is usually just a few metres deep, and is exposed to intense sunlight and higher salinities. At low tide many of the reef-flat areas are exposed to air, and often there are seagrasses interspersed among the corals.

Reefs can also take several different forms on a larger scale. When they grow right along a coast they are called fringing reefs because they fringe the edges of an island or continent. When sea levels rise low coastlines are flooded and a fringing reef may be able to grow upwards to keep up with the higher sea level. At that point the reef is separated from its original coastline and becomes a barrier reef. An atoll is a special kind of barrier reef that forms around an oceanic island. It starts as a fringing reef around the island, and as the island slowly erodes away the reef continues to live. Eventually the island disappears, leaving only a reef in the middle of the sea enclosing a shallow lagoon.

Sometimes many reef types are found in the same area. Reefs exposed to the open sea shelter shallow areas behind them, called patch reefs. These have different environmental factors, depending on the currents that pass through the area, the topography of the land behind them and the water clarity. Each of those different areas often hosts different complexes of organisms. It is interesting to visit various reef types and find an assortment of different corals, fish, invertebrates and other animals in each one.

ZOOXANTHELLAE

The amazing richness and diversity of a coral reef is built on the many relationships that have evolved to allow life to exist in the relative deserts of tropical seas. Without these relationships a reef would lose its ability to support the wealth of species that makes it so interesting and valuable. The most fundamental relationship is the one between the coral polyp and its symbiotic algae – the zooxanthellae (see also page 42). Even though corals have their own tentacles and stinging cells, there is not enough food in the water for them to derive energy to build their skeletons. The algae produce the sugars that the corals need to survive, and in turn get a safe place to live within the tissues of the corals.

SPONGES

Sponges are found everywhere along a reef. Many divers are familiar with large barrel sponges that can protrude magnificently from a reef slope, but sponges occupy almost every niche on a reef. It has long been known that they produce many interesting chemicals for self-defence. These are sought by nudibranchs, which accumulate the defensive chemicals for their own use, and by medical researchers, who look for new medicines in the compounds. Recent research has shown that sponges play a near-equal role to that of the zooxanthellae in feeding the reef ecosystem. Sponges expel their filtering cells on a constant basis, thus providing food for many filter feeders along the reef (de Goeij et al., 2013).

Opposite: Reef flats are ofen exposed to the air during low tide. Only the toughest of organisms can survive the heat, dessication and increased salinity from the daily tides.

Below: Sponges are ubiquitous on the reef but some species can grow to enormous dimensions.

FISH

Fish occupy almost every niche on a reef and fulfil many roles in maintaining the function of reefs. Schools of fish swimming above a reef slope are often feeding on plankton in the water. Other fish can be seen picking or scraping at corals for the polyps themselves, some feed on the algae that live among the corals and others are predators at every level. If one type of fish is lost from a reef, it can have consequences for the rest of the reef. If the herbivorous fish like parrotfish (Scaridae) and rabbitfish (Siganidae) are all removed, algae can grow unchecked and quickly overwhelm the corals and smother a reef. Abundant algae on a reef are usually a sign of an unhealthy reef system.

The magnificent Humphead Wrasse (*Cheilinus undulatus*) is one of the few natural predators, along with the Triton Shell (*Charonia tritonis*), of the Crown-of-thorns Starfish – a voracious predator of live corals. When Humphead Wrasse are removed from a reef the starfish is free to reproduce and can form infestations that eat the live coral polyps from vast areas of reef, leaving only dead white skeletons in their wake.

Above: The Steephead Parrotfish (*Chlorurus microrhinos*) is one of the most common large parrotfish in the Coral Triangle.

Top: The largest bony fish on coral reefs, Humphead Wrasse, are one of the key predators of Crown-of-thorns Starfish.

Left above: The Goldlined Spinefoot (*Siganus guttatus*) is a common herbivore on Coral Triangle reefs.

Left: The Triton Shell is prized in the curio and shell trade and is becoming rare on Coral Triangle reefs.

Opposite: The Crown-of-thorns Starfish is a voracious predator of coral polyps. An outbreak of the starfish can eat all the corals on a reef in weeks. A 40 cm (16 in) female can spawn up to 400 million eggs in a single night.

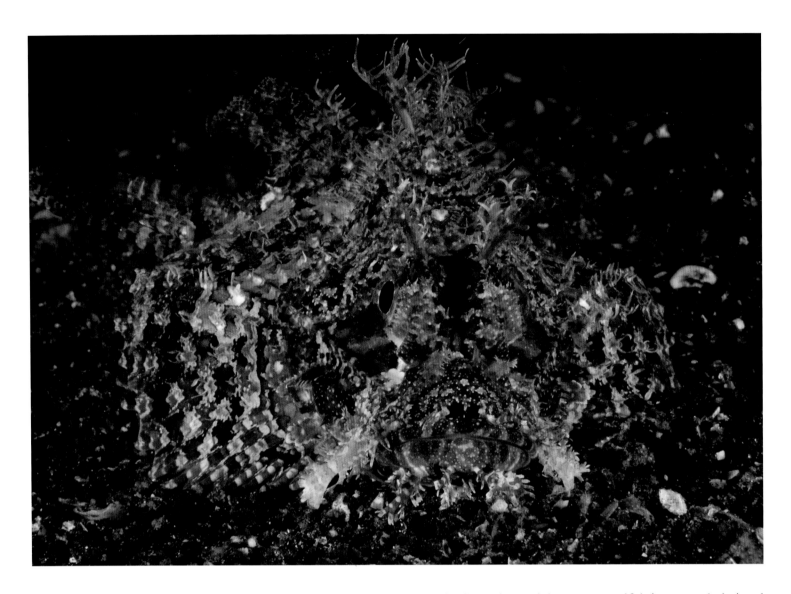

REEFS' SHAPES AND COLOURS

The richness of shapes and colours is another defining characteristic of a coral reef. Coral forms and shapes are largely determined by the amount of wave energy that a coral colony experiences and the available light. In deep or turbid areas the corals are often spread out in wide plates to gather as much light as possible. Corals near a reef crest or reef flat are exposed to waves and need to be robust, with relatively thick branches. At depth, where the wave action does not reach, they can be finer and more delicate.

The abundance of colours on a reef is a curious affair. Seawater is an extremely effective filter of sunlight, but it is filtered differently for different parts of the spectrum. Red light is almost entirely lost within the first 10 m (33 ft), but blue light penetrates to almost 200 m (656 ft) in clear waters. However, when you shine a torch light on many animals at depth, you find them to be bright red – does their colour provide them with a kind of science-fiction cloaking device? Without red wavelengths available, there may be no visual evidence for other fish to pick up. Combined with intricate patterns, a red-coloured fish may be invisible below 10 m (33 ft).

It has been observed that many angelfish (Pomacanthidae) and parrotfish employ complementary colour patterns, particularly blue and yellow. When it comes to intricate patterns, it has been shown that at close range they may be particularly conspicuous, but at a distance they can act as an effective camouflage (Marshall, 2000).

VALUE TO HUMANS

Besides their intrinsic value of existing to support their own ecosystem, coral reefs have particular values for humans. In 1999 it was estimated that coral reefs had a global value of US $6,075 per hectare per year (Costanza et al., 1997) because of fisheries, coastal protection, tourism and other services. The direct value of coral reefs comes from the food security they provide, particularly to impoverished communities on small islands, from fisheries and from tourism. Reefs also give value from the pharmaceutical products that have been discovered or may be discovered in the chemicals produced by organisms on reefs. Indirect values of coral reefs come from the protection they provide to the coastlines behind them, and from the nursery function they play for fisheries offshore.

This page: Angelfish are a diverse group of tropical fish with flashy colours. The contrasting colours may help the fish to remain invisible in open water or against the backdrop of the reef.

Opposite: The combination of the complex morphology, colour patterns and shades of red may render this scorpionfish invisible at depths beyond 10 m (33 ft).

SEAGRASSES *and* MANGROVES

SEAGRASSES and mangroves are two important Coral Triangle habitats that are often overlooked by tourists and conservationists, but they are increasingly being included in tour packages for diving and birdwatching, and prioritized in conservation programmes. Both habitats are among the most valuable in the world, and provide numerous benefits to humans and other ecosystems. They contain the only flowering plants to inhabit marine ecosystems, and are widely distributed around the world. Seagrasses and mangroves are often closely associated with coral reefs in the Coral Triangle region, and many fish species utilize all three habitats during at least one of their life-history stages.

SEAGRASSES

These are the only vascular flowering plants that have adapted to being completely submerged in seawater. Some species resemble grass, with long, blade-like leaves, but they are not grasses and are more closely related to lilies and gingers. While they can be found in every sea (except in cold polar waters), they are generally restricted to shallow coastal waters where light can penetrate. Global seagrass richness is quite low, with only about 60 species worldwide, but the Coral Triangle region has the highest diversity, with at least 19 species (Orth, Carruthers, & Dennison, 2006; Short, Carruthers, Dennison & Waycott, 2007). Many seagrass meadows are found in coastal estuaries or on the tops of reefs, but they can occur at depths of more than 50 m (165 ft) in some locations.

Seagrasses tend to grow in areas with soft bottom sediments like sand or mud. They develop intricate systems of rhizomes that connect individual, self-contained plants (ramlets), which help to stabilize the sediments. Each ramlet is a fully functioning clone with leaves and roots, connected to other clones via horizontal underground rhizomes (McKenzie, 2008). When seagrasses grow on top of a coral reef, this stabilizing function helps to keep the sediment off the corals. The seagrasses not only stabilize the sediment, but also trap sediment that can come from land. This serves to build new land areas and can also help to maintain the water clarity needed for coral reef growth.

Most plants get their nutrients through their roots from the soil, and photosynthesize by exchanging gasses from their leaves. Gas transmission in seawater is much less efficient than it is in air. Seagrasses have adapted a special cuticle that surrounds each leaf, and gas is exchanged through the cuticle rather than the stomata as in terrestrial plants. The leaves contain small air pockets that help with gas exchange and keep the leaves afloat (Hogarth, 2007). The vascular system in each leaf is broken in several compartments, preventing the entire plant from flooding with seawater if a leaf is broken.

Seagrasses have also adapted to reproduction underwater, and can reproduce sexually or asexually. For reasons that have yet to be explained, they do not engage animals for pollination as terrestrial plants do, so they usually produce only tiny flowers since there is no need to attract pollinators. Seeds, when they are produced, are thought to not travel far beyond the parent plant. The rhizome structure is another avenue for seagrass reproduction. The rhizomes transport hormones and genetic material, and extend into suitable habitat where

clones can establish themselves. A seagrass bed is thus often a large area of a single species or even a single cloned plant (Hogarth, 2007).

There is intensive competition for space on a coral reef, with some corals actually attacking and killing a neighbouring coral, then invading its space. In the dark of night, when predators cannot see, the aggressor coral will extend its tentacles to the neighbouring victim and kill the polyps within reach. However, corals and seagrasses seem to have a truce. In areas where corals and seagrasses coexist, there is often a halo of sand between the coral and the plant. It is the tropical marine equivalent of a demilitarized zone.

Above: Dense meadows of seagrass are important habitats for the juveniles of many fish species, and for Green Sea Turtles and Dugongs.

Opposite: Low tide exposes reef tops and allows people to glean the area for small fish, shells and other invertebrates.

Above: The Pinkfish Sea Cucumber (*Holothuria edulis*) is one of the most sought-after species as a food item: it has now become rare in many areas.

Top: Where corals are found in seagrass meadows there is often a halo of sand around the coral colony.

Above right: The Common Yellow Seahorse (*Hippocampus taeniopterus*) is often found among seagrass blades.

While shallow seagrass meadows do not have the species diversity of coral reefs, they are important for many organisms, including sea cucumbers, seahorses (Syngnathidae), Green Sea Turtles and Dugongs. The primary production of a seagrass meadow is among the highest in the world, and has been compared to the production of corn and sugar cane. Many commercially important fish and prawns shelter in seagrass meadows in their juvenile forms. One species of burrowing shrimp (*Alpheus edamensis*) has been documented in Indonesia to use nearly half of all seagrass leaf production in seagrass meadows to line its burrow and to eat (Hogarth, 2007).

Seahorses, Green Sea Turtles and Dugongs are some of the best-known and most charismatic organisms that occupy seagrass meadows. Seahorses, while looking sweet and docile, are predators. They use their camouflage and their prehensile tails when lurking among the seagrass leaves, waiting for unsuspecting prey. Green Sea Turtles and Dugongs are herbivores that feed among the meadows. Both species need large amounts of seagrass, and have developed strategies for ensuring that they do not deplete their food resources completely.

Turtles prefer the youngest growth of the seagrass, which is at the bottom of the leaf closest to the sediment. That leaf area is the most digestible and has the fewest epiphytes. A turtle may occupy a single seagrass meadow for several weeks, essentially mowing the grasses and cropping them close to the sediment. This promotes new growth of the leaves, but over time it weakens the rhizomes. After several weeks or a month, when the leaves and rhizomes stop responding quickly to the cropping, the turtle moves on and finds a new patch of seagrass to exploit while the previous one recovers.

Dugongs employ a different strategy. A Dugong ploughs a meandering path through a seagrass meadow as it consumes the entire plant – leaves, rhizomes and roots. Dugongs seem to be able to detect the plants with the thickest and most nutritious rhizomes. The new scar in the seagrass bed opens space for younger growth. When multiple Dugongs are feeding in the same meadow their paths never cross, and they usually leave at least 1 m (3 ft) of intact vegetation between them (Hogarth, 2007).

Aside from trapping sediment, seagrasses perform many other important ecological functions. In ecology the term primary productivity is applied primarily to plants and algae, and refers to their rate of generation of biomass, or biological material, in an ecosystem. When seagrasses are in close proximity to coral reefs, as is often the case in the Coral Triangle, their high primary productivity provides energy to the reefs. Many fish species split their time between the seagrass and reef ecosystems. As the fish feed on the seagrass, then move back to the reef, they essentially move the metabolized energy of the seagrass to the coral reef through their waste output or as prey.

MANGROVES

Not so long ago the word 'mangrove' was almost always followed by 'swamp'. A mangrove swamp was generally considered to be a forbidding place, impenetrable and filled with disease-carrying insects. Mangrove forests were only appreciated by a handful of biologists and the local communities that knew the riches that they held. Now, mangroves are widely accepted as one of the three richest and most productive tropical marine habitats, along with seagrasses and coral reefs. They are now much more likely to be described as a wetland or forest.

Mangrove can be a tricky term. It can refer either to the habitat of partially flooded forests and vegetation that lies between dry land and the sea throughout the tropics, or to the salt-tolerant shrubs and trees that dominate the habitat. Globally, there are about 60 plants that can be found only in the tropical intertidal area. These are known as 'true mangroves', and Southeast Asia and the Coral Triangle have the highest number of species, at 42.

Altogether there are slightly more than 250 total plant species that have been identified in the mangrove forests of the Coral Triangle, including orchids, ferns and palms. Four of the Coral Triangle's six countries rank among the top 15 of the world's mangrove countries, with Indonesia having the biggest mangrove area in the world. The mangrove forests of southern New Guinea, shared between Indonesia and Papua New Guinea, are among the largest and most intact mangrove forests in the world.

Table 2: Mangrove area by Coral Triangle country in 2000

Country	Mangrove area (ha)	Global rank	Per cent of global total
Indonesia	3,112,989	1	22.6
Malaysia	505,386	6	3.7
Papua New Guinea	480,121	8	3.5
Philippines	263,137	15	1.9
Solomon Islands	47,100[1]	No data	No data
Timor Leste	3,035[2]	No data	No data
Giri et al., 2010.			

[1] Albert, J. A. and Schwarz, A. J., 2013. Mangrove Management in Solomon Islands: Case Studies from Malaita Province. CGIAR Research Program on Aquatic Agricultural Systems. Penang, Malaysia. Policy Brief: AAS-2013–2014.
[2] Timor Leste CTI National Coordination Committee.

Right: The blue water mangroves of Indonesia's Raja Ampat islands grow in close association with coral reefs.

Opposite: Mangroves provide an important habitat for small fish and invertebrates that seek shelter among their prop roots.

Below: Mangroves like these in the Solomon Islands provide essential building materials for coastal communities in the Coral Triangle.

Like seagrasses, true mangrove species have adapted to living in a harsh salt-water environment. Unlike seagrasses, mangroves cannot be completely submerged and need air for transpiration. They can survive in the saline environment because their roots are able to exclude some salt from entering the tree, they have some tolerance to having salt concentrations in their tissues and they have special mechanisms for eliminating salt through their leaves. Not all species employ all of these adaptations, and some even extend roots until they find a lens of less saline water to tap.

Because the muddy, water-saturated soil that mangroves tend to prefer is low in oxygen, many mangrove species employ special roots to enable some oxygen absorption from air. The typical stilt roots of many species, or the knees and root ends that are exposed to air, give a tree the ability to absorb oxygen needed for respiration. It is these structures that make a mangrove forest nearly impenetrable.

In the Coral Triangle mangroves can be found in a number of habitats and soil types. The largest stands often occur at river mouths and estuaries with muddy soils. Along coasts without heavy wave action, they can form a narrow or wide belt between the low- and high-tide lines. They are also commonly found, in smaller stands, behind coral reefs, where the bottom type is usually sandier. The species composition frequently shows distinct zones, from areas most exposed to the sea and in deeper water, to those in the high-tide line or upstream, where wave action is lower and freshwater inputs are more common. Across these zones the dominant mangrove plants change as the habitat and physical parameters change.

Mangrove forests are rich in animal life. At low tide it is easy to see several species of snail and other molluscs. Crabs are easy to spot in mangrove forests. Fiddler crabs (*Uca* spp.) can be seen displaying their oversized claw as they proclaim their territory on the muddy bottoms at low tide, and Mud Crabs (*Scylla serrata*) are an important commercial animal for human consumption.

Mangroves are home to a rich assortment of fish species, but several species stand out. The archerfish (*Toxotes* spp.) are a group of fish commonly found in mangroves (as well as other habitats). They have evolved to spit a jet of water from just below the water's surface, for a distance of up to 1.5 m (5 ft), in order to dislodge insects from low branches.

Even more characteristic of Coral Triangle mangroves are the mudskippers (several genera of the Gobiidae family). Mudskippers are amphibious fish that have adapted to spend most of their time on mangrove mudflats at low tide, or to climb onto mangrove roots at high tide. Their pectoral fins have adapted for walking, and in some species have fused together to form a kind of suction cup. They dig burrows in the mud and hunt for all sorts of prey, while some are more focused on foraging for leaves. At low tide mudskippers can be seen maintaining their territory on the mud. They often

Above: The flat dorsal sides of Banded Archerfish (*Toxotes jaculatrix*) allow them to hunt just below the water's surface. They overcome significant parallax to shoot a jet of water at insects resting just above the water.

Top: Fruit and leaf litter fall from mangroves helps build a thick layer of carbon-rich sediment, making mangroves one of the best places for carbon sequestration (see page 58).

engage in territorial displays or outright combat to maintain their territory. Recent studies indicate that some mudskipper species are air breathers and have specially adapted vascular systems in their skin that absorb oxygen, and the adult fish will transport air bubbles into their burrows.

Mangroves harbour an assortment of large vertebrates, including mammals and reptiles. Within the Coral Triangle some mangrove forests along the coasts of Sumatra are still home to ever-dwindling populations of Sumatran Tigers (*Panthera tigris sumatrae*). Unique to Borneo are Proboscis Monkeys (*Nasalis larvatus*), which were once thought to be mangrove specialists, but are now known to occupy other habitats – they keep mostly to forests near water. A variety of other monkeys and cats can be found in mangrove forests, but none is a mangrove specialist.

The biggest predator of the Coral Triangle's mangroves is the Estuarine Crocodile, or Saltwater Crocodile (*Crocodylus porosus*). Estuarine Crocodiles are the world's largest reptiles and are known to prey on everything from fish and birds, to humans when available. They can grow to up to 7 m (23 ft), and there are unsubstantiated reports of individuals reaching 9–10 m (30–32 ft). Females build nests on dry land and guard them closely until they hatch. It has been noted that crocodile movements through the channels may move enough mud to increase the productivity of the ecosystem.

Above: Mudskippers (*Periophthalmus* spp.) are gobies that can breathe air and hunt for insects on exposed mud flats and mangrove areas.

Below: The Estuarine Crocodile is the largest living reptile and is revered in parts of the Coral Triangle as a representative of ancestors.

BENEFITS OF SEAGRASSES AND MANGROVES

Mangroves play an important role, as do seagrasses and coral reefs, in coastal protection. By trapping and consolidating sediments that are brought down rivers and washed off the mainland, mangroves help to build new coastlines. They also protect against waves and storms that continuously pound the shore, and prevent erosion. There is even some evidence that sites with intact mangroves fared better during the 2004 Asian tsunami than areas where the forest was degraded.

Seagrasses and mangroves, together with temperate salt marshes, form some of the most important carbon sinks on the planet. As carbon dioxide accumulates in the atmosphere, conservationists are searching for ways to reduce the effects. Some ecosystems process atmospheric carbon and lock it away for the long term – thus sequestering it away from the atmosphere. Growing trees use and sequester large amounts of carbon. Planting trees and keeping forests standing are two strategies for reducing atmospheric carbon dioxide.

However, some coastal ecosystems may lock carbon away faster than fast-growing tropical rainforests. Mangroves and seagrasses do not lock much carbon in their tissues – they are much smaller than gigantic rainforest trees. However, they transport vast amounts of carbon into the mud and sediment below them at very high concentrations. Seagrasses, mangroves and temperate salt marshes are now thought to store the equivalent of half of the global transport sector's annual carbon emissions (Nellman et al., 2009).

Mangroves and seagrasses are critical habitats for maintaining fisheries. Throughout the Coral Triangle many small islands have local communities that have learned to exploit the richness of these two habitats for their survival. It is a common sight to see an entire village out exploring the seagrasses during low tide, searching for snails, sea cucumbers, fish and other animals to eat or sell. Mangroves have long been a source of wood, for construction and cooking, for local communities. Both habitats are also critical for commercial fisheries.

Many tropical shrimp and fish species use mangroves and seagrasses as juvenile habitat. Almost all shrimps caught in mangroves are juveniles of species that are usually caught in deeper waters offshore. The complexity of the stilt roots, knees and pneumatophores makes it difficult for larger predatory fish to hunt, and provides protection for the small juveniles of both shrimp and fish. Without mangroves to act as habitat for the juveniles, it is likely that many fisheries would suffer.

Above: Mangrove wood is an important building material and fuel source for many Coral Triangle communities.

Left: Replanting mangroves can help control erosion on small islands.

Above: Communities in the Solomon Islands are learning to manage mangroves and replant areas that have been overharvested.

Left: Mangrove roots in wet muddy sediments cannot exchange gases necessary for growth so some roots, called pneumatophores, grow above the sediment and exchange gases when they are exposed at low tide.

OTHER HABITATS

THE Coral Triangle is most commonly associated with the three richest habitats of coral reefs, seagrasses and mangroves. However, these three habitats form only a tiny portion of the Coral Triangle's total sea area, and are not fully representative of all the habitats in the region. The other habitats are much less studied, but despite being less species rich they are just as important. Beaches, shallow mudflats, deep benthic muddy bottoms, the open seas, oceanic trenches and seamounts are all important habitats of the Coral Triangle.

BEACHES AND MUDFLATS

Beaches and mudflats are coastal habitats that form at the margins of the land and sea, and they are sometimes closely associated with coral reefs and mangroves respectively. Sandy beaches often form on the tops of coral reefs and can become large enough to support some vegetation and an island. The sand is an accumulation of coral rock, shells of all sorts, and other material pounded by waves, and deposited by the digestive systems of parrotfish that scrape corals in search of algae.

Sandy beaches are a critical habitat for sea turtles, which return to the beaches of their birth to deposit eggs that will become the next generation. The sex of the turtles is dependent on the temperature of the nest. Cooler nests produce more male hatchlings. If the vegetation at the edge of the beach is destroyed, an island loses its stability and erodes more quickly – consequently the turtle nests normally shaded by the vegetation will produce more and more females. The sandy beaches are naturally unstable. The sand is dynamic and the action of waves, water currents and storms moves the sand around an island and up and down the beach. The width of the beach changes with the season, and over decades an island can migrate backwards and forwards across the top of a reef.

In the coastal zone, often associated with river deltas and mangroves, there are often large, shallow areas with a very gradual gradient into the sea. These areas, which are frequently exposed and dry at low tide, are known as tidal flats, mudflats or sandy flats. They are an essential part of the tropical marine ecosystem but are understudied and undervalued, perhaps because they appear to be barren and lifeless. Mudflats support large amounts of life that have

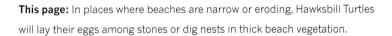

This page: In places where beaches are narrow or eroding, Hawksbill Turtles will lay their eggs among stones or dig nests in thick beach vegetation.

Opposite: The Horned Sea Star (*Protoreaster nodosus*) is a predator found on sandy bottoms and in seagrass beds. It has been observed consuming sponges, corals, sea urchins and snails.

Right: Yellow Shrimp Gobies (*Cryptocentrus cinctus*) share their burrows with *Alpheus* shrimps. The shrimp maintains the burrow and the fish act as security guards.

Above: The Bat Volute (*Cymbiola vespertillo*) is a predatory gastropod that prowls the sandy floor around coral reefs.

Left: The Bobbit Worm (*Eunice aphroditois*) is an ambush predator that buries itself in the sediment until an unsuspecting prey brushes an extended tentacle. The attack has been known to cut prey completely in half.

evolved to cope with the stresses of daily inundation and drying, salt accumulation and lack of oxygen in the muddy substrate. Many species of mollusc, echinoderm and worm inhabit the mud and are supported by cyanobacteria, sometimes called blue-green algae, that photosynthesize. These mudflats support large populations of seabirds and waders, often as they migrate from the tropics back to high-latitude breeding grounds (Miththapala, 2013).

OPEN OCEANS AND SEAS

Beyond the coastal habitats is the largest part of the Coral Triangle's marine realm – the open oceans and seas. Within the Coral Triangle there are several deep basins and two major continental shelf areas. The Sunda and Sahul Shelves are vast areas attached to the Asian and Australian continents, respectively, which rarely exceed 200 m (656 ft) in depth. The Sunda Shelf is overlain by the South China Sea. The Sahul Shelf lies beneath the Arafura Sea and the Gulf of Carpentaria. Beyond the shelves are the deep basins of the Sulu, Sulawesi (Celebes), Banda, Molucca, Flores, Bismarck and Solomon Seas (Longhurst, 2007), some of which are more than 3,000 m (9,840 ft) deep.

The Sunda Shelf lies between mainland Asia, Sumatra, Borneo and Java. During the last ice age the shelf area was largely exposed and comprised wetlands and forests. Some animals were able to migrate between the islands. Likewise, the Sahul Shelf connected Australia and New Guinea. Now both areas are rich fishing grounds for commercial fishing.

The deeper basins and seas can reach depths of several kilometres, and include some deep oceanic trenches. Light can only penetrate seawater to a maximum of 200 m (656 ft). Beyond this life exists based on energy that descends from the lighted, photic zone. A food chain exists in the deepest waters but it is mostly unknown. The open ocean has very little nutrient input, and even phytoplankton struggle to maintain an existence. Most of the energy to support life beyond the photic zone originates from dead material that sinks into the dark. But even in this harsh environment there is significant life.

Life in the deep sea's upper layer is heavily influenced by water motion. The major flow of water through the Coral Triangle is the Indonesian Through-flow, which conducts waters from the Pacific Ocean to the Indian Ocean. However, due to the complex topography, number of islands and shifting seasonal monsoon winds, surface currents in the Coral Triangle are extremely complex, with various side currents and medium-scale eddies throughout. There are various areas of strong upwellings and downwellings, generated when the Indonesian Through-flow encounters an island or an underwater ridge. The changing monsoon winds alter the surface currents further, complicating the pictures and generating more upwellings and downwellings. With all of this complexity, plankton concentrations vary accordingly (Longhurst, 2007).

One of the greatest migrations on Earth is the daily migration of zooplankton from the darker depths towards the surface of the sea as the sun sets. Small pelagic fish, including anchovies and sardines,

Left: The Chambered Nautilus (*Nautilus pompilus*) spends its days in deep, dark waters but comes to the shallows at night to feed. There is increasing concern about populations as they are caught for the curio trade and for food.

feed on the zooplankton wherever they can be found. The food chain is completed by large predators, including several tuna and mackerel species, billfish and sharks. Because of the lack of hiding places in the open seas, organisms must employ other methods to avoid predation. Many plankton species are transparent. Fish are often silvery to reflect the surrounding waters and hence become invisible. Small pelagic fish school for defence, finding safety in numbers. Larger fish use countershading, with dark dorsal sides and white undersides, to blend in from above and below (Goltenboth, Timotius, Milan & Margraf, 2006).

There are giants that survive lower on the food chain. Whale Sharks (*Rhincodon typus*) are the world's biggest fish, but they feed on plankton. Several sites in the Coral Triangle, including the

Left: Trevallies and jacks hunt shoaling anchovies that come to Raja Ampat with favourable currents that bring nutrients.

Opposite top: Fish and invertebrate larvae are one of the main components of zooplankton communities riding currents around the Coral Triangle.

Opposite below: The world's largest shark, the Whale Shark filters plankton and small fish from the water it sucks into its massive mouth.

Philippines' Sorsogon Province and Indonesia's Cenderwasih Bay, host concentrations of Whale Sharks when they aggregate to take advantage of annual plankton blooms. One of the rarest sharks in the world, the Megamouth Shark (*Megachasma pelagios*), is also a filter feeder. While it seems to be found throughout the world, 12 of the 55 confirmed sightings since 1976 have been in the Coral Triangle.

The Sulawesi Sea and the Western Pacific Ocean between the southern Philippines and Papua New Guinea are critical for the world's tuna fisheries. This area acts as a spawning and nursery ground for Western Pacific tuna including the Southern Bluefin (*Thunnus maccoyii*), Albacore (*T. alalunga*), Bigeye (*T. obesus*), Yellowfin (*T. albacares)* and Skipjack Tuna (*Katsuwonus pelamis*).

SEAMOUNTS

Scattered among many of the seas are hundreds or thousands of seamounts. These are underwater volcanic mountains that reach at least a kilometre (3,280 ft) from the bottom of the sea, but are often much taller and sometimes nearly break the surface of the sea. When they do break the surface, they become volcanic islands.

Seamounts are important habitats for many species, and points of reference for long-ranging migratory species. Locating and studying seamounts is a difficult process, and very few in the Coral Triangle are well known. It has been estimated that Papua New Guinea has 91 seamounts and the Solomon Islands has 157 (Allain et al., 2008). Another estimate projects that there may be as many as 2,246 seamounts within the claimed waters of the countries of the Western Central Pacific Ocean (Pitcher, Morato, Hart & Clark, 2007). Indonesia's Banda Sea is a hotspot of tectonic and volcanic activity, with hundreds of seamounts. Gunung Api (Fire Mountain) is a seamount that rises from 4,000 m (13,123 ft) deep to become a volcano in the middle of the Banda Sea – it is an example of a seamount that has emerged from the sea.

The seamounts of the Coral Triangle, like seamounts elsewhere, are important ecological features. As deep currents of the Indonesian Through-flow race between the islands, they hit the seamounts and are forced upwards. The resulting upwellings bring nutrients from the sea floor towards the surface and underpin an oasis of life. The abundance of life on a seamount attracts schools of big fish, sharks, turtles and whales. Indeed, the waters of the southern Banda Sea and the Savu Sea, shared between Indonesia and Timor Leste, appear to be a globally unique hotspot of marine mammal diversity, with 13 species identified around Timor Leste (Dethmers et al., 2012), 15 species in the Alor Strait region of Indonesia and 20 in Komodo National Park. Indonesia has recorded 29 total species, including Blue Whales (*Baleanoptera musculus*) and Sperm Whales (*Physeter macrocephalus*) (Khan, 2014).

Right: The tops of undersea mountains or pinnacles can be covered by coral reefs, while steep sides plunge to great depths.

This page: Indonesia's Gunung Api (Fire Mountain) rises 5,000 m (16,500 ft) from the depths of the Banda Sea. This remote island is home to 23 species of bird and large populations of sea snakes. The former include Brown Boobies (*Sula leucogaster*), above, and the latter Black-banded Sea Kraits (*Laticauda semifasciata*), left.

3

INDONESIA

Eighteen per cent of the world's coral reefs are found in Indonesian waters (Spalding, Ravilious & Green, 2001). This vast archipelagic country spans more than 5,000 km (3,107 miles) from west to east, straddles the boundary between the Pacific and Indian Oceans, and contains more than 17,000 islands. With 251 million people, Indonesia is by all accounts the largest country in the Coral Triangle. It is the result of complex tectonic action as several oceanic and continental plates collided. At either end of the country shallow seas cover relatively shallow continental shelves, while in the centre there are several distinct seas with deep trenches that can exceed more than 1,000 m (3,280 ft) in depth. This complex geology also results in frequent earthquakes and the presence of many active volcanoes spread throughout Indonesia.

Left: Blue and Gold Fusiliers (*Caesio caerulaurea*) form schools along reef edges to hunt for plankton in the water column. They are a favourite target of illegal fish bombers.

INDONESIA

Right: Many of Indonesia's islands are formed by volcanoes like these on the island of Bali. Indonesia's southern islands are seasonally dry and lack the rainforests associated with many of the country's other islands.

Above: Dense rainforest covers many small islands that dot the archipelago.

Left: Coconut palms are often a sign of human habitation as they are planted for their many uses, including building material and food.

Indonesia's marine biodiversity is stunning. It has attracted the interest of naturalists from the early days, when Alfred Russel Wallace first sailed into Ambon Bay and described the magnificent corals observable through the clear waters. Coral reefs are found throughout Indonesia, but vary considerably in richness and distribution related to the underlying geology and ocean currents. The country also boasts larger mangrove and seagrass areas than the other Coral Triangle countries.

Western Indonesia, comprising the large islands of Sumatra, Java and Borneo (Kalimantan covers more than 70 per cent of Borneo island), sits on the edge of the Eurasian tectonic plate's Sunda Shelf. The South China Sea and Java Sea lie between these large islands, with depths rarely exceeding 200 m (656 ft). Corals fringing the islands are less developed than those in other parts of Indonesia particularly because the large islands are drained by major rivers carrying heavy loads of sediment that limit coral growth. Most coral-reef formations in the Sunda Shelf region grow further offshore from the large islands, where the waters are clearer.

Another large shelf, this one an extension of the Australian Plate, forms the far eastern extremity of Indonesia. The Sahul Shelf underlies the Arafura Sea and the eastern Indonesian provinces on New Guinea, Papua and West Papua. The reefs at this end of Indonesia are well developed, extremely rich in species and considered by many scientists to be the global pinnacle of marine biodiversity. At least 550 of Indonesia's 590 hard coral species and 1,300 coral-reef fish have been counted in this region's Raja Ampat archipelago.

Between the two shelves are several deep basins, the geographically complex island of Sulawesi, the Lesser Sunda archipelago and the Molucca Islands. Within this area of central Indonesia there are at least 27 deep basins and ocean trenches. Takabonerate, in the middle of the Flores Sea, at 220,000 ha (543,632 acres) is the third largest atoll in the world. With clear waters and swift currents bringing larvae into this area, the coral reefs are well developed and rich with biodiversity. These deep basins are also of critical importance to many large whale species, including Blue and Sperm Whales that migrate here on an annual basis.

Top: Mandarin Dragonets (*Synchiropus splendidus*) come together in quick mating displays.

Right: Seagrasses, corals and mangroves can be found living in close proximity throughout the Raja Ampat archipelago.

Opposite: Soft corals (class Octocorallia) resemble plants but are colonial animals related to gorgonian sea fans and sea pens. Some species are an important food item for Hawksbill Turtles.

The PEOPLE

GIVEN Indonesia's place as the world's largest archipelagic nation, it is not surprising that fish and fisheries constitute a critical component of its food security and economy. Almost 60 million people live within 30 km (19 miles) of a coral reef (Burke, Reytar, Spalding & Perry, 2012). Indonesia's population is ethnically diverse, with more than 300 recognized ethnic groups. The Javanese are the largest group, and nearly 57 per cent of Indonesians live on Java. In comparison, the Papuan and Maluku Provinces comprise 20 per cent of Indonesia's land area, but are home to only 2 per cent of the population. This imbalance gives rise to many challenges in managing fisheries. Small islands with few people and few resources depend on the sea for daily livelihoods, while getting fresh fish to feed overpopulated Java is a constant struggle.

Indonesia's economy relies on its marine environment and marine resources, including mining, oil and gas, and tourism. Slightly more than half of the country's animal protein comes from fish, and 95 per cent of the fish is produced by artisanal fishermen (FAO, 2013). One-third of the fish production comes from aquaculture featuring seaweed and shrimps as two of the main marine resources primarily under cultivation. High-value export fisheries, including tuna, shrimp and groupers, earned Indonesia US $2.5 billion in 2010.

Above right: Seaweed can be grown on lines that float with the aid of empty PET bottles. Income from seaweed farming can supplement or replace fishing and can be more reliable.

Right: Red Groupers (*Plectropomus* spp.) are highly prized in Chinese cuisine and if kept alive can bring much more income than common reef fish. This drives some fishermen to use increasingly destructive methods to catch them.

MARINE SPECIES DIVERSITY

EXPEDITIONS surveying marine biodiversity in Indonesia regularly discover new species of fish and invertebrate. In 1997 a couple on their honeymoon noticed a strange fish in the Manado, North Sulawesi, fish market. The fish was subsequently identified as a previously unknown species of the 'living fossil' coelacanth. It had been thought to be extinct until it was discovered living at great depths along the south-east coast of Africa. The fish caught in Manado was designated as a new species, *Latimeria menadoensis*. Since the initial sighting less than ten individuals have been caught and documented in the same area of North Sulawesi. Some years later, in 2013, scientists working for Conservation International off the island of Ternate discovered a new species of bamboo shark, *Hemiscyllium halmahera*. While similar to other members of its genus, this new species was distinctly different in colour and pattern.

The seas of Indonesia are a global hotspot for marine mammals. Twenty-two species of cetacean and one sirenian have been recorded in the country, with more found in the eastern Indonesian seas than in the western portion. The passages between the islands of the Lesser Sundas are important migratory corridors for baleen whales. Blue Whales use the Banda Sea as a calving ground, and Sperm Whales are known to use the Sulawesi Sea and the north coast of Papua as a feeding ground. Dugongs were once spread throughout Indonesia, but populations are now severely depleted (Dirhamsyah et al., 2012).

In 2012 a group of experts on Indonesian marine biodiversity helped the government to identify priority areas for conservation that were most deserving of investment for marine biodiversity conservation. This select group of marine scientists and conservationists provided data and ranked each of the 12 marine ecoregions that make up the Indonesian archipelago. The ecoregions were assessed for the irreplaceability of their biodiversity, vulnerability and how well they represented Indonesian and global biodiversity. Species richness and endemism, and the presence of vulnerable species, were considered important attributes in the prioritization.

The resulting priorities are grouped into five tiers. The highest priority area was clearly the Papuan ecoregion. The Lesser Sundas, Banda Sea and Sulawesi Seas made up the second tier. At the bottom of the ranking were two ecoregions, the Strait of Malacca and the southern Java coast (Huffard, Erdmann & Gunawan, 2012). This ranking, while important and useful for biodiversity richness, does not take into account uses of the sea. Setting priorities based on fisheries may produce a very different ranking.

Above: The Weedy Pygmy Seahorse (*Hippocampus pontohi*) was first described in 2008. It is one of the few pygmy seahorses to live on algae rather than corals.

Above: Nantucket whalers would venture as far as the Coral Triangle to hunt Sperm Whales (*Physeter macrocephalus*). The deep basins and trenches of the Coral Triangle are an important hunting habitat for these ocean giants.

Right: With more than 10,000 islands, Indonesia is a diver's paradise. Corals near the surface often face strong waves and must be thick and robust.

Opposite: Using live-aboard boats is the only way to visit many of Indonesia's best and most remote dive sites. Divers can sometimes spend up to four hours a day in the water but must be careful because some areas can have extremely strong currents and medical assistance can be far away.

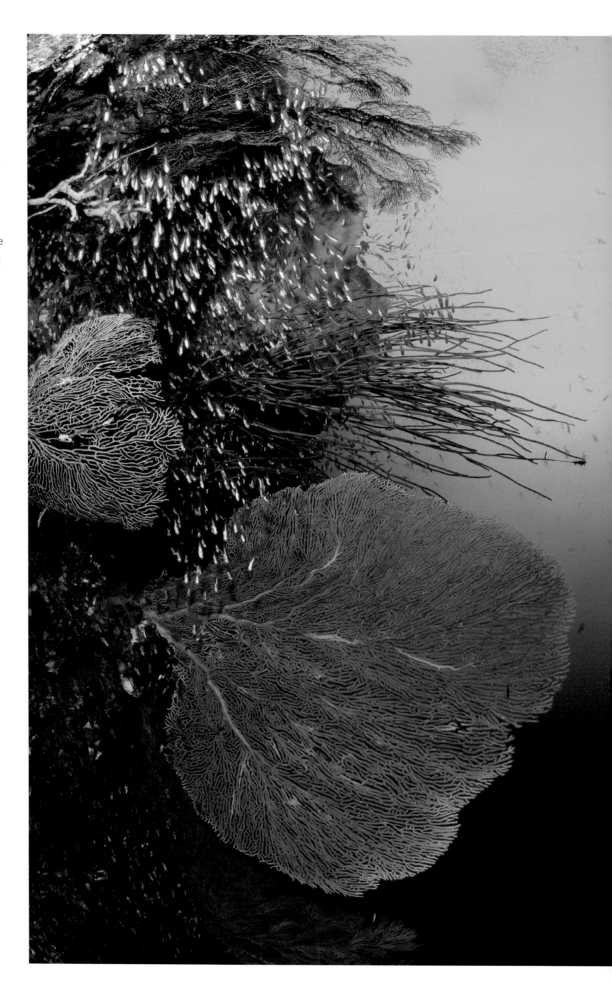

DIVING

OASTAL and marine tourism is a major part of the Indonesian economy, and SCUBA diving is possible almost everywhere. Nearly every large island has at least one dive centre, and remote areas are accessible via numerous live-aboard boats that ply every Indonesian sea. Diving in this vast archipelago can be suited to absolute beginners with numerous opportunities for lessons, or catered to the most experienced divers searching for strong currents, rare animals, remote locations and unusual sights. Many of the most popular diving areas are in national parks and protected areas. Komodo National Park, Wakatobi National Park and Bunaken National Park are all major diving destinations and on the wish lists of most divers.

Many of Indonesia's diving areas offer opportunities to see particular species that are hard to find in other places. Perhaps the most famous of these areas is the world-famous Lembeh Strait near Bunaken National Park at the northern tip of Sulawesi. Besides the usual reef life, Lembeh Strait has a black-sand bottom generated by the nearby volcanic activity. On these sandy bottoms divers can encounter some of the most sought-after photographic targets and unusual species, including the Starry Night Octopus (*Callistoctopus luteus*), Mimic Octopus (*Thaumoctopus mimicus*), Cockatoo Waspfish (*Ablabys taenianotus*) and the weird-looking Hairy Frogfish (*Antennarius striatus*).

This page: A Harp Shell (*Harpa major*) in Lembeh Strait preys on a crab. The shell has been known to detach part of its foot when pursued, then turn to attack when the original predator begins to eat the detached foot.

Left: The black sandy substrate of Lembeh Strait in North Sulawesi is famous for unusual species such as this Hairy Frogfish.

Below: The Starry Night Octopus is primarily nocturnal but can be conspicuous on the black volcanic sand of Lembeh Strait.

Bali is the centre of Indonesia's tourism industry and well known for its nightlife and culture. It also has many dive resorts on the north and south coasts. Several dive sites stand out, including the wreck of the USS *Liberty*. Lying on its side, just off Bali's north coast, this wreck is accessible from the beach. It is now covered in soft and hard coral growth, and teeming with small fish and moray eels (Muraenidae). On the south coast, divers can brave surprisingly cold waters from July to October to encounter the massive Ocean Sunfish (*Mola mola*). These giants can reach up to 1,000 kg (2,205 lb) and travel all the way to Nusa Penida to have their dead skin and parasites removed by resident cleaner wrasses.

At the northern tip of Sumatra, Pulau Weh is washed by strong currents from both the Indian Ocean and the Andaman Sea. While Indonesia's most famous dive destinations are found in the east, Pulau Weh offers dramatic underwater scenery and the chance to see several species of shark, eagle rays (Myliobatidae) and manta rays (*Manta* spp.). Batee Tokong, one of Pulau Weh's most famous dive sites, is teeming with moray eels.

At the far eastern end of the Lesser Sunda archipelago, Pulau Alor is an increasingly popular diving destination. This area, known for strong currents and most suitable for experienced divers, offers a diverse array of tiny animals to schools of hammerhead sharks (Sphymidae).

Above right: The Barred Moray Eel (*Echidna polyzona*) is known to feed primarily on small crustaceans.

Right: Divers can regularly encounter Ocean Sunfish in cold-water upwellings around Bali during the season from August to October.

Left: Sometimes forming huge schools, Scalloped Hammerhead Sharks (*Sphyrna lewini*) can look intimidating but are not considered dangerous.

Below: Anchovies school over a reef to protect themselves. However, many predators have developed techniques for attacking such a bait ball.

Several diving resorts are nestled among the 31 islands of East Kalimantan's Derawan Islands. Situated on the east coast of Borneo at the northern end of the Makassar Strait, the Derawan Islands are known as a critical Green Sea Turtle and Hawksbill Turtle rookery. Sangalaki Island is famous for concentrations of manta rays feeding on the plankton-rich waters, while nearby Kakaban has a brackish water lake in the middle of the island with thousands of stingless jellyfish and a peculiar medusivorous (jellyfish-eating) anemone species.

Above: A Broadclub Cuttlefish (*Sepia latimanus*) prowls the reef off East Kalimantan's Sangalaki Island.

Right: Four species of stingless jellyfish inhabit the brackish lake on Kakaban Island in East Kalimantan.

Opposite: The White Sea Anemone (*Entacmaea medusivora*) lives in Kakaban Lake and feeds on stingless jellyfish. Its Latin species name, *medusivora*, means jellyfish eater.

Indonesia has so many dive sites that it is impossible to pick a single top destination, but Raja Ampat would be a top contender in any discussion. It is a group of four main islands surrounded by more than 1,000 cayes and islets, and was relatively unknown until the early 2000s. This stunning archipelago at the extreme north-western tip of New Guinea was surveyed in 2001 and quickly became one of the ultimate dive destinations. Intact coral reefs, one of the highest rates of biodiversity in the world, sharks and seasonal anchovy migrations made Raja Ampat's reputation. Now divers have a selection of resorts on several islands as well as many live-aboard options, most of which depart from Sorong. The flight from Jakarta to Sorong takes five hours. Speedboat transfer to the islands can take another five hours. The journey may be long, but the destination is worth the effort.

Above: Indonesia's marine biodiversity benefits from the warm, clear waters that surround its thousands of islands.

Right: Schools of anchovies move in unison in an attempt to confuse or intimidate potential predators.

MARINE ENVIRONMENT THREATS

INDONESIA faces many of the threats faced by the rest of the Coral Triangle. Pressures from densely populated islands, local and international demand for seafood, the race to develop quickly and climate change all result in a degraded marine environment. Indonesia faces particular threats from overfishing and habitat destruction.

Indonesian coral reefs are highly threatened by local stresses and global change. The 'Reefs at Risk Revisited in the Coral Triangle' report estimated that 93 per cent of Indonesian reefs are facing threats from destructive fishing, overfishing, pollution or development. The effects of overfishing are worst on coastal reefs

and reefs nearest to population centres, but evidence of overfishing is also seen on remote reefs. Blast fishing is a widespread practice threatening nearly 80 per cent of Indonesia's reefs. Pollution from urban centres without sewerage treatment, and run-off from uncontrolled logging and mining, are also major threats (Burke et al., 2012).

Indonesia manages its fisheries through a system of 11 'fisheries management areas' defined by the central government. The Ministry of Marine Affairs and Fisheries assesses fish stocks in each area and reports according to several species groups. Of 69 separate assessments of fish stocks, 48 were thought to be over-exploited or fully exploited. This widespread over-exploitation included most shrimp fisheries, demersal fisheries, small pelagic fisheries and most tuna fisheries. Only some shrimp fisheries in eastern Indonesia, Skipjack Tuna and squid fisheries were not fully exploited. Coastal areas throughout Indonesia, where 85 per cent of fishing activity occurs, are the most overfished areas (Dirhamsyah et al., 2012).

Hunting, collecting, fishing and habitat destruction result in threats to many Indonesian marine species. All of the sea-turtle species – Leatherback, Green Sea, Hawksbill, Olive Ridley, Flatback (*Natator depressus*) and Loggerhead (*Caretta caretta*) – found in Indonesia are protected, but threats remain from egg poaching, loss of nesting beaches, and by-catch in gill-net, trawl and long-line fisheries. A study by WWF documented that 95 per cent of eggs were poached from nests in East Kalimantan in 2009 and 2010 (Anonymous, 2014).

Above: Lost or discarded fishing nets are a major threat to coral reef organisms in the Coral Triangle. The plastics used in modern fishing gear do not decompose and continue to kill for years.

Right: Dogtooth Tuna (*Gymnosarda unicolor*) are one of many prized tuna species in the Coral Triangle.

MARINE RESOURCE MANAGEMENT

WITH such a vast marine area, more than 17,000 islands, and millions of fishermen and other users of the sea, managing Indonesia's marine resources can be a daunting task. Managers must balance the nutritional and livelihood needs of communities spread across a vast archipelago against the finite capacity of the resources to continue to provide.

Three main national agencies are responsible. The Ministry of Marine Affairs and Fisheries was established in 1999 to develop, manage and conserve fisheries resources. The Ministry of Forestry is responsible for managing most mangrove forests and all national protected areas, including marine areas. The State Ministry of Environment, along with the Ministry of Forestry, is responsible for coastal environmental protection. Besides these there are numerous other government agencies with some responsibility for marine resources. At the national level there are another 18 ministries, state ministries, line agencies and councils with mandates to manage marine resources. This is further complicated by the official policies of devolving management responsibility to provinces and local-level governments since the early 2000s. As part of the process of decentralizing coastal management, fishermen and local communities are often encouraged to join management efforts (Siry, 2011).

Indonesia's first marine protected areas were established in the 1970s as national parks and were off limits to almost all users. They proved to be unpopular with local communities, which usually relied on the areas for food and livelihoods. At the launch of the CTI in 2009, Indonesia's President Susilo Bambang Yudhoyono made a commitment to establish 20 million ha (49.4 million acres) of marine protected areas by 2020, doubling a previous commitment to reach 10 million ha (24.7 million acres) by 2010. This goal was reached in 2009, and by 2011 an estimated 17.2 million ha (42.5 million acres) had been declared as some sort of marine protected area, the vast majority being either Marine National Park or District Marine Conservation Area (Carter, Soemodinoto & White, 2010).

Above right: Fishermen in Bali assist each other to take their boats to the sea every morning.

Right: Fishing with pole and line is generally considered less destructive, but if left unchecked it can deplete fish populations.

NATIONAL PLAN *of* ACTION

As mentioned opposite, President Susilo Bambang Yudhoyono was the instigator of the CTI. The National Plan of Action closely mirrors the Regional Plan of Action (see page 33) with its five goals and associated targets. Indonesia was the only Coral Triangle country to have previously committed to seascape conservation through engagement in two multilateral ecoregion programmes, the Sulu-Sulawesi Marine Ecoregion and the Bismark-Solomon Seas Ecoregion programmes. Recognition that marine-resource management goes beyond jurisdictional boundaries is as important within Indonesia's vast archipelago as it is with its neighbours. The Banda-Sunda and Savu Seascapes are prioritized in the national plan.

The commitment to an ecosystem approach to fisheries management is strong in Indonesia, and as in the case of the regional plan, focuses on legislation, improving livelihoods for poor coastal communities, and management of tuna and live reef fish. A particular emphasis is placed on eliminating 'illegal, unreported and unregulated' fisheries. Planned activities revolve around building capacity within local communities to monitor and enforce fishing regulations collaboratively with government agencies.

Marine protected areas are a high priority for the Indonesian government, with the ambitious target of 20 million ha of marine protected area by 2020 (see opposite). It is not just having more total area that is important. Indonesia plans to distribute the areas throughout important regions, to represent critical habitats by engaging in an analysis of where there are gaps in the system, and to improve management in existing and new areas. To ensure that the system is functioning, the national plan also calls for the development of robust monitoring and evaluation mechanisms that are standardized throughout the country.

The action plan for endangered species calls for specific action on marine turtles, sharks, Napoleon Wrasse and marine mammals. An important aspect of the plan is the creation and training of a Wildlife Crime Unit to investigate and apprehend persons suspected of wildlife crimes.

Above: Collecting data about turtles is critical for their survival.

Left: Fan corals (Gorgonacea) usually grow in areas with strong currents.

PROTECTED AREAS

INDONESIA'S protected areas comprise both terrestial and marine environments. Marine protected areas cover more than 17.2 million ha (42.5 million acres), roughly 5 per cent of Indonesia's territorial waters. Nine of Indonesia's 50 national parks are predominantly marine.

BUNAKEN NATIONAL PARK

One of Indonesia's earliest and best-known marine parks and conservation areas is Bunaken National Park. The 89,095-ha (220,154-acre) park was established in 1991 and quickly became a well-known diving destination renowned for its rich reefs and abundant fish populations. The forests of Manado Tua island, which lies within the park, are home to one of the few remaining populations of the Crested Macaque (*Macaca nigra*). Underwater there are more than 8,000 ha (19,768 acres) of coral reefs, extensive seagrass beds and important mangrove forests. The area is home to populations of Dugongs, Sperm Whales, Orcas and the only known population of the Indonesian coelacanth. The park comprises two areas straddling the North Sulawesi capital of Manado. The northern portion surrounds five islands of mostly volcanic origin. The southern portion borders the Sulawesi mainland coast just south of Manado. There are 22 villages within the borders of the park, with 30,000 inhabitants.

For the first nine years of its existence, the Ministry of Forestry's Department of Nature Conservation, based in Jakarta, managed the park. Rules were made in Jakarta and the local communities had very little input. During this period, despite the declaration of the park, monitoring showed that the coral reefs were degrading through overfishing, pollution and the continued use of blast fishing, and mangroves were being cut at an alarming and unsustainable rate. The events of the late 1990s changed things in Bunaken. When President Suharto resigned, a new era of Indonesian government began with new laws decentralizing decision making. At the same time the United States Agency for International Development was conducting a major natural-resources management project in Bunaken.

Several studies identified that the zones instituted by the previous regime were too complicated and that there were conflicting zoning plans. Decentralization also meant that funds generated in the park could be kept in the area rather than being sent to the national government. A process was started to rezone the park and to develop an entrance-fee system that would bring much-needed income and development to the residents of the park.

The ensuing process revolutionized marine protected areas in Indonesia and became a model for protected areas throughout the region. In 2000 the Bunaken National Park Management Advisory Board was established and became a key model for collaborative management between many government agencies, the private sector, local communities, academia and NGOs. The new management advisory board comprised seven government agencies from local government and the national government, the North Sulawesi Watersports Association and the Bunaken Concerned Citizens Forum, among others.

The first task was to rezone the entire park. The new management body conducted an intensive process that included extensive community consultations. More than 35 meetings were held with communities on Bunaken Island alone just to agree to the draft zones. Eventually the new zones were supported by an innovative fee system that charged for entrance to the park,

granting a one-year pass to purchasers. The funds from the entrance fee, supplemented by allocation from the national government and donors, helped to establish a patrolling system that quickly eliminated the most destructive fishing and harvesting practices in the park. A portion of the revenue was also allocated to a small-grants fund to assist villages with development projects (United Nations Development Programme, 2012).

While Bunaken is certainly one of the best marine protected area success stories in the region, it continues to face challenges as it works towards effective and meaningful management. The close proximity of Manado's 400,000 people puts constant pressure on the park to provide fish and timber. The park continues to struggle to contain and manage refuse disposal in the sea and litter that keeps on accumulating on beaches (Sidangoli, Lloyd & Boyd, 2013). WWF-Indonesia helps with anti-litter campaigns and continues to work with the management body to coordinate between the government, local communities and diving industry.

Above: Manado Tua is one of the islands in Bunaken National Park at the northern tip of Sulawesi.

Opposite: Longfin Bannerfish (*Heniochus acuminatus*) school above the reef as they hunt for plankton in the water column.

Right: One of the goals of the Alor Marine Protected Area is to improve fisheries for small-scale fishermen and to ensure that future generations also have access to rich fisheries.

Opposite: Jef Pele is one of the islands of Raja Ampat's Misool Marine Protected Area.

KARIMUNJAWA MARINE NATIONAL PARK

The small archipelago of Karimunjawa lies in the centre of the Java Sea. More than 100,000 ha (24,710 acres) of the archipelago form the Karimunjawa Marine National Park. In 2002 the Wildlife Conservation Society set up programmes to help curtail rampant destructive fishing, using cyanide and dynamite, to supply the live reef-fish trade. Studies of the reef-fish populations, habitat condition and fishing activities were conducted, and helped to inform a rezoning of the park in an effort to curtail the destructive practices. However, by 2009 it was clear that they were continuing.

An urgent need for strategy change led WCS and the government managers to engage local fishermen on a financial basis. Programmes to build fish cages supplied by grouper hatcheries reduced pressure on wild populations. Village laws were passed to reduce conflict between spear and hand-line fishermen. The spear fishermen were banned from taking three species of grouper that were key for the live reef-fish trade. Within several years, surveys showed wild grouper populations rebounding inside the park area (Muttaqin & Campbell, 2014).

SOLOR AND ALOR

At the far eastern end of Flores Island a group of small islands includes Solor and Alor Islands. The area now has a 400,000 ha (988,422 acre) marine protected area with very specific objectives of protecting fish resources. A major part of WWF-Indonesia's engagement in the area since 2006 centres around applying concepts of ecosystem-based management of fisheries. Assessments of turtle by-catch in gill-net and purse-seine fisheries in the area help managers to teach fishing communities how to avoid catching turtles, and what to do when they find a still-living turtle in their nets. Three fishing companies are now helping to collect data on Skipjack Tuna fisheries to better inform management decisions, and fishermen are being trained in better methods of handling fish. If a tuna is handled properly after being caught, it can earn a fisherman more income, which means that he does not need to go to sea as often or catch as many fish. After a single training session it was found that fish quality increased by 50 per cent.

RAJA AMPAT

New Guinea's distinctively shaped western peninsula, often referred to as the Bird's Head, is surrounded by the most biodiverse waters in the world. Cenderawasih Bay separates the peninsula from the rest of New Guinea to the east. The northern, western and southern shores of the Bird's Head Peninsula are bordered by the Pacific Ocean, Halmahera Sea and Ceram Sea respectively. There are four large islands and thousands of tiny islets. The lush, steep-sided limestone outcrops are unmistakable as Raja Ampat. Together, these seas and their many islands make up Raja Ampat.

The Bird's Head Seascape is a global priority for marine conservation because of the very high levels of species richness found there. Surveys conducted in 2001 and 2002 by Conservation International and TNC identified 1,635 coral-reef fish species and more than 600 coral species. Seventy per cent of the world's coral species can be found in the waters of Raja Ampat. Several islands around Raja Ampat host important nesting grounds for Green Sea Turtles and Hawksbill Turtles, and one of the biggest remaining Leatherback Turtle nesting beaches is at Jamursba Medi on the northern coast of the Bird's Head Seascape.

In the decade since the first coral-reef surveys, Raja Ampat has become a premier diving destination and a leader in marine conservation, but the area still faces grave threats. The remoteness and low population density of Raja Ampat had kept the coral reefs, mangroves and seagrasses in better condition than most in Southeast Asia. However, as resources were depleted in other parts of Indonesia, fishermen, loggers and miners discovered the region just as conservationists had (Agostini et al., 2012). In 1999 there were 20 documented lift-net boats. By 2005 that number had increased to 250, and all of the boats were manned by fishermen from other parts of Indonesia (Huffard et al., 2012). Blast fishing, cyanide fishing and shark finning began to seriously impact fish populations.

Several conservation organizations, including TNC, Conservation International and WWF-Indonesia, teamed up to save the Bird's Head Seascape. Together, they agreed to work towards a network of marine protected areas across the seascape, to improve fisheries management, to help the local government implement a functioning zoning system, and to conserve iconic and threatened species. TNC and Conservation International focused on Raja Ampat, while WWF-Indonesia made the Leatherback Turtles a priority.

Above: Yellowbanded Sweetlips (*Plectorhinchus lineatus*) hunt invertebrates at night and rest during the day.

Top and left: Soft corals do not form hard skeletons to build a reef but still rely on zooxanthellae to supplement energy.

Above: Bigeye Snapper (*Lutjanus lutjanus*) are frequently found schooling with other species of snapper as they hunt fish and crustaceans.

Left: Longfin Batfish (*Platax teira*) school in the open water near a reef. These omnivores eat plankton, small invertebrates and algae.

Customary and traditional management systems are pervasive among the Melanesian communities of Papua. TNC and Conservation International, together with the local governments and other partners, decided to combine the traditional management systems with the latest science and an intensive awareness campaign to protect the reefs of Raja Ampat. By 2007 awareness campaigns had borne fruit and several communities had agreed to protect parts of their coral reefs. Combined with an existing marine protected area managed by the National Department of Forestry and Conservation, the new network of protected areas covered an impressive 895,210 ha (221,2112 acres) of sea area, with extensive coral reefs, seagrasses and mangroves included (Agostini et al., 2012). Several of the protected areas were expanded in 2009 to total 1,185,940 ha (293,0527 acres).

In 2007 the local government of Raja Ampat fully acknowledged the wishes of the local communities to protect their resources, and consolidated the six protected areas into the Raja Ampat Marine Protected Area. This consolidation mandated that each protected area in Raja Ampat must have its own management unit, and that the units must operate as a single entity. The local government formed new agencies to tackle the tasks of managing the protected area network and funding it.

The NGOs contributed by helping to develop management plans that would incorporate the goals of the protected areas and provide livelihoods to the local communities. Eighteen studies of the ecology, economics and social situation of the region were conducted as part of the decision-making process. Zoning is one of the key tools for managing such a large network of marine protected areas. Establishing zones for strict protection, for non-destructive fishing, mariculture and other uses, minimizes conflict between users and allows for better controls governing each use. It can be alarming to see fishing in a marine protected area, but if the zoning allows for fishing in some areas it can be acceptable.

A zoning plan for the 366,000-ha (904,406-acre) Southeast Missol protected area was launched in 2012. The local communities launched the plan with support from the local government, tourism companies, a local pearl farm and NGOs. There are core zones of completely protected areas, zones of traditional management where some fishing is allowed for local community use and mariculture zones. As in the case of other areas of Raja Ampat, local community patrol groups have been established, trained and endorsed by the local government. The patrols are funded in part through a system where divers buy an annual pass before they can dive in the Raja Ampat Marine Protected Area network (Mangubhai, 2012).

An important component of the conservation effort in Raja Ampat is the role of education. West Papua province has an extremely high population growth rate of 5.5 per cent. TNC and Conservation International recognized that many young people will be making choices in several years about how they use the resources of Raja Ampat. In 2008 they refitted a retired tuna long-line boat to become a floating classroom called the *Kalabia*. This boat was to visit all the 100 villages in Raja Ampat with education programmes about the marine environment and conservation. Children get the opportunity to participate in a three-day programme that includes a well-designed curriculum and experiential learning activities such as snorkelling, and visits to critical ecosystems (Conservation International, 2011).

One of the best examples of the Raja Ampat government's commitment to marine conservation came in February 2013 with the declaration of its entire 4.6 million ha (11.4 million acre) sea area as a shark sanctuary. The sanctuary declaration protects sharks and manta rays in Raja Ampat from fishing or any trade in their parts in the region. The government determined that the potential income from tourism was more profitable than that from shark finning, and was swayed by a successful petition campaign led by two NGOs, WildAid and Shark Savers, in partnership with local divers and NGOs.

Shortly after the designation of the Raja Ampat shark and manta-ray sanctuary, the Indonesian Ministry of Marine Affairs and Fisheries announced its intention to follow the provincial regulation. Manta rays have long benefited from possessing bad-tasting flesh and were never the target of any major fishery. In recent years, however, their gills have become a feature of Chinese medicinal practice and demand has soared. It has been estimated that manta-ray tourism generates US $15 million per year in Indonesia, while manta-ray hunting only earns US $570,000. The law was declared on 28 January 2014 to ban the fishing, killing, harming and trade of manta rays throughout Indonesia, with a penalty of up to one year in jail or a fine of US $25,000.

THE LESSER SUNDA ECOREGION

The islands of the Lesser Sundas are one of Indonesia's top marine biodiversity conservation priorities after the Bird's Head peninsula. This archipelago stretches from Bali to Timor Leste and covers more than 45 million ha (111 million acres) of sea and land. The ecoregion is known for its rich coral reefs, but it is also the place where the Indonesian Through-flow empties into the Indian Ocean, resulting in massive currents between the islands. The south sides of the islands are battered by the open seas of the Indian Ocean, and in the centre of the islands lies the deep basin of the Savu Sea. Upwellings bring nutrient-rich waters to the edges of the islands, and this attracts abundant schools of fish, which further attract giant species. Twenty-one species of marine mammal, including Blue and Sperm Whales, inhabit the waters of the Lesser Sunda Ecoregion (Wilson, Darmawan, Subijanto, Green & Sheppard, 2011).

Above: The islands of Komodo National Park are dry and arid for much of the year.

Parts of the ecoregion have been well known for many years. Komodo National Park may be one of Indonesia's most famous natural attractions, not only for the legendary Komodo Dragons (*Varanus komodoensis*) of Komodo and Rinca Islands, but also for the stunning underwater beauty and diversity. The coral reefs around Bali and its protected areas are also well known. The Indonesian government and NGOs have been partnering for decades to establish and improve the management around these protected areas, and more are being established on a regular basis.

In 2011 TNC, working with the Ministry of Marine Affairs and Fisheries, published a plan for a network of marine protected areas in the Lesser Sunda Ecoregion that would protect marine resources and local livelihoods, and be resilient in the face of future climate-change impacts. The eventual plan incorporated 37 existing protected areas, along with 19 already proposed areas, and identified another 44 areas that need protection. An important consideration in this ecoregion was the inclusion of unusual 'deep but near-shore' habitats, where coastal habitats are in very close proximity to deep trench waters. This

may help to bring cooler water to sensitive coral-reef habitats and protect them from the harmful effects of climate change-associated warming (Wilson, Darmawan, Subijanto, Green & Sheppard, 2011).

The Ministry of Marine Affairs and Fisheries established the Savu Sea National Marine Park in 2009. The declaration of this 3.5 million ha (8.15 million acre) park pushed Indonesia past its commitment of 10 million ha (24.7 acres) of marine park by 2010. The park is divided into two areas. The smaller area spans the Sumba Strait and links Sumba and Flores Islands. The larger area protects the southern boundary of the Savu Sea and links Sumba with Timor to the east. The communities bordering the Savu Sea remain some of the most remote and poorest in Indonesia. Even though the population is relatively small there are threats to the area, including overfishing and destructive fishing (Wilson et al., 2011).

With the declaration of the park a management plan was required. Unfortunately, this area is quite remote and very little data was available. TNC Indonesia spearheaded a process to engage local communities throughout the park to build awareness about the park and marine resource management while also gathering input into an eventual zoning system for the park. TNC employed a technique called 'participatory mapping' to engage the communities. Within eight weeks from December 2010 until March 2011, TNC teams visited 110 villages around the new marine park. Data about habitats, endangered species and uses of the Savu Sea were mapped in order to better understand the needs of the biological system and to balance that with the needs of the communities (Syofyanto, Farjariyanto & Koliham, 2011).

Another key area in the Lesser Sunda Ecoregion is being tackled through a partnership between WCS and local governments in West Nusa Tenggara province. Sandwiched between Bali and Komodo National Park are the two large islands of Lombok and Sumbawa. The province had a loose network of marine protected areas that suffered from a lack of effective management. As WCS helped to assess the management needs it found local communities and government agencies eager to designate more protected areas.

The area is experiencing a surge in tourism as people venture out of popular Bali. Coral reefs, beaches and surfing are increasingly popular on the south coast of Lombok in Bumbang Bay. Traditional livelihoods targeted the reef fish and lobsters along the coast, and tuna in the deeper Indian Ocean waters. Fishermen were resorting to using up to 45,000 traps to capture juvenile lobsters, then raising them in cages. WCS studies identified the potential for the lobster fishery to improve and become sustainable. The local community and government established a 23,000-ha (56,834-acre) marine protected area, and WCS is providing support for the fishermen to improve their lobster fishery so that it is sustainable, thus increasing their incomes (Kartawijaya, 2014).

Above: The long spines of the Common Lionfish (*Pterois volitans*) can deliver a strong toxin. With such a stout defence, the fish knows few predators as an adult.

Right: Blue-spotted Stingrays (*Dasyatis kuhlii*) give birth to live young and may live for up to 18 years.

Left: Sea pens (*Pteroeides* spp.) are grouped with soft corals and live as colonial organisms. The central 'stalk' is a single specialized polyp with other polyps having specialized functions in the colony.

Below: Whip Gobies (*Bryaninopes yongei*) live in pairs exclusively on the Black Whip Coral (*Cirrhipathes anguina*).

MARINE FISHERIES MANAGEMENT

BESIDES working to protect endangered species and establish marine protected areas, NGOs in Indonesia now focus more and more attention on sustainable fisheries. Part of the efforts underway in Indonesia represent a major change in thinking about how to approach marine fisheries management and reflect a movement seen in other parts of the world. In the past conservationists often identified the worst, most destructive and most damaging fisheries, and attempted to regulate them or shut them down. While this approach may still be appropriate in many cases, WWF-Indonesia is also engaging with fisheries and companies that are taking steps to improve their practices and incorporate sustainability into their business models. This is only possible due to the efforts of many organizations over the past 20 years to raise awareness around the world to the facts of overfishing, and to create a demand for sustainably sourced seafood.

The current gold standard for sustainable fisheries is the Marine Stewardship Council's certification. A fishery that fulfils all the criteria set by the council is considered to be using the best practices for ensuring that the fish stock is stable, that the environment is not damaged and that management practices are effective. In 2008 WWF-Indonesia established the Seafood Savers project, working with fisheries and fishing companies that are committed to improving their business and ultimately aiming to achieve sustainability. A highlight of their work focuses on tuna.

Indonesia is one of the world's biggest tuna-producing countries and ships much of its product to the United States and Japan. It is a complex fishery with several species targeted throughout the archipelago, and fleets using several techniques and gears. Purse-seines, long-lines and pole-and-line operations target Skipjack, Bigeye and Yellowfin Tuna. Issues with by-catch in long-line fisheries are well known. A study by WWF in 2005 estimated that Indonesia's Pacific long-line fishery was catching between 256 and 768 Leatherback Turtles per year. Purse-seine fisheries are also culprits in producing by-catch, especially when the nets are set on floating objects designed to attract fish. In 2010 WWF-Indonesia and the Ministry of Marine Affairs and Fisheries conducted a pre-assessment of Indonesian tuna fisheries to determine what kind of task would need to be completed to achieve the Marine Stewardship Council's certification for each fishery.

The assessment concluded with some positive aspects about Indonesia's tuna fisheries, such as relatively low impacts on the ecosystem, while urgent actions were needed to improve governance and management, and garnering of information on stock status. The resulting action plan is heavy on addressing management issues, and data collection and research needs. Since then the Ministry of Marine Affairs and Fisheries, with help from WWF-Indonesia, has released an action plan for moving forwards with sustainable and responsibly managed tuna fisheries.

In the meantime WWF-Indonesia has been helping with some of the actions through its Seafood Savers platform and other projects. To help address the lack of information about tuna stocks, WWF-Indonesia, the Marine Conservation Science Institute and scientists from the Indonesian government tagged 43 tuna in the waters around Wakatobi National Park, South Sulawesi, in 2010 and 2011. The tags are miniature electronic-data recorders that monitor temperature, depth and light levels. Large tuna were tagged with pop-up tags that release from the tuna after one year and automatically upload their data to a satellite for further analysis. Smaller tuna were implanted with a device that will record data for up to two years.

In the Solor Alor region WWF-Indonesia is working with local communities to eliminate a new and disturbing method of fishing tuna using home-made explosives. A comprehensive programme of marine protected areas, alternative livelihoods and marine-conservation awareness is being employed to make the tuna fishing in this remote and highly biodiverse region sustainable. As part of the Seafood Savers project, WWF-Indonesia signed an agreement with the first company to join in 2012. Sea Delight, a US-based seafood importer, agreed to engage in Fishery Improvement Projects throughout Indonesia, and to work with fishermen, middlemen and other suppliers to improve the handling of fish as it moves from fisherman to consumer. Sea Delight and WWF-Indonesia are working together with tuna hand-line fishermen in East Java to reduce by-catch and improve their catch quality. As more and more consumers in Indonesia and beyond demand responsibly caught seafood, programmes like Seafood Savers will make an exemplary link to sustainable fisheries.

Opposite: Yellow Glassy Sweepers (*Parapriacanthus ransonneti*) form large schools under overhangs or in caves during the day and disperse at night to feed.

4

MALAYSIA

Malaysia is unique within the Coral Triangle because it is the only one of the six countries that does not form part of the Pacific Ring of Fire. The rest of the Coral Triangle is subject to severe earthquakes and volcanic activity, but Malaysia sits firmly on the Sunda Shelf of the Asian continental plate. The most populous part of the country is Peninsular Malaysia in the west, attached to mainland Southeast Asia. Across the South China Sea to the east are the states of Sabah and Sarawak on the island of Borneo. With coasts bordering the Strait of Malacca, and the Andaman, South China, Sulu and Sulawesi Seas, Malaysia has a long coastline and high marine biodiversity, even though reef formation is limited along much of the coast. The vast majority of Malaysia's reefs are found in Sabah, with most of the remainder fringing the isolated islands on the east coast of Peninsular Malaysia.

Left: *Acropora* corals provide habitat for many species of damselfish, anthias and wrasses at Sipadan Island.

MALAYSIA

THAILAND

Gulf of
Thailand

Andaman
Sea

Payar

George Town

Perhentian Islands
Redang Islands

Kuala Terengganu

Tenggol

Peninsular Malaysia

M A L A Y S I A

KUALA LUMPUR
Endau

Tioman
Islands

Malacca

SINGAPORE

I N D O N E S I A

Sunda shelf

200m
2000m
4000m
6000m

Towns/cities

National parks

0   200 Miles

0   300 Kilometres

Palawan

PHILIPPINES

Tun Mustapha Park (proposed)

Banggi

Sulu Sea

Kudat

Lankayan

Tunku Abdul Rahman Park

Kota
Kinabalu

Turtle Islands
Sandakan

S a b a h

Lahad Datu

BRUNEI

Tun Sakaran Marine Park
Semporna

Pom Pom
Si Amil

Mabul

Sipidan

Sulawesi
Sea

S a r a w a k

B O R N E O

Kuching

Kalimantan

Malaysia is a multicultural crossroads with a mix of ethnicities, religions and languages to match its rich biodiversity. The federation was formed when the 11 states of newly independent Malaya, Singapore, Sabah (then called North Borneo) and Sarawak joined together in 1963 to form Malaysia. Singapore soon left the federation. Under the terms of the federation, Sabah and Sarawak have some autonomy over natural resources, including marine resources.

Peninsular Malaysia's west coast is separated from Sumatra, Indonesia, by the Strait of Malacca. This strategically important navigation channel is lined by mangrove forests on both sides and has minimal coral-reef growth. Nearly 45 per cent of Malaysia's fish landings come from the Strait of Malacca, making it a critical water body for the country's food security.

The east coast of Peninsular Malaysia is exposed to the open waters of the South China Sea, and intense wave energy from the annual monsoons that bring high winds and rain from October to March every year. The coastline is dominated by long, sandy beaches, and the numerous offshore islands are surrounded by fringing reefs. Further offshore, the drowned Sunda Shelf extends all the way to Borneo, giving Malaysia extensive yet relatively shallow fishing grounds.

Malaysia's two largest states, Sabah and Sarawak, are on Borneo, the world's third largest island, which also houses Indonesia's Kalimantan provinces and the Sultanate of Brunei Darussalam. Sarawak occupies the south-western lobe of Borneo with a long coastline fronting the South China Sea. Its coast is characterized by

the many estuaries formed by large rivers draining the state's extensive tropical rainforests and mountainous spine. The numerous major rivers carry large sediment loads that limit coral growth.

Above: Sabah's east coast has long expanses of pristine white beaches with little development.

Opposite: Many ships have sunk on the reefs of the South China Sea and remain to be discovered.

Sabah, at the northern tip of Borneo, borders three seas. Seventy-five per cent of Malaysia's coral reefs is found around the coast and islands of Sabah. The majority of Sabah's coral reefs are concentrated around the south-eastern corner of the state in Semporna district and around its northernmost twin peninsulas. Sabah's long South China Sea coastline is also fringed with extensive reefs and several small island groups, and Sabah contains the majority of Malaysia's mangrove forests.

Above: Boheyan Island in Sabah's Semporna District is an important stop-over for Bajau Laut people, the sea nomads.

Left: Seagrass beds in the sheltered bays of Mantanani Island were once important feeding grounds for migrating Dugongs but not many remain in most of their range.

Opposite: Peninsular Malaysia and Sabah have long stretches of beaches, making them an important habitat for nesting sea turtles.

THE PEOPLE

THE majority of Malaysia's 30 million people live in Peninsular Malaysia, with 3.5 million in Sabah and 2.5 million in Sarawak. The country enjoys a high literacy rate of 93 per cent, and had one of the Coral Triangle's highest per capita gross domestic products, at US $17,000 in 2012. Fossil fuels, timber, palm oil, rubber and tourism dominate the economy. In 2013 approximately 110,000 people were directly employed in the fisheries industry.

Above: The Bajau Laut, sea nomads, spend their entire lives at sea. The back corner of this boat is the kitchen.

Below: Small villages are occasionally erected when migrant fishermen move to an island for several months.

KEY MARINE ANIMALS

MALAYSIA does not have the extensive reef area of some of its larger Coral Triangle neighbours, but its reefs are rich with coral and fish species. Surveys have documented nearly 500 species of coral throughout Malaysia. A single expedition in Semporna, Sabah, in 2010, documented more species of mushroom coral than in the next richest spot, Raja Ampat, Indonesia. Results from fish surveys indicate that Semporna is among the top five sites in the world for fish richness.

Four species of marine turtle nest throughout Malaysia. The most numerous are the Green Sea Turtles and Hawksbill Turtles. The Turtle Islands, near Sandakan town on Sabah's east coast, are shared with the Philippines and are among the most important locations for nesting Hawksbill and Green Sea Turtles in the Coral Triangle. The islands have been designated as Southeast Asia's first trans-boundary protected area, forming the Turtle Islands Heritage Protected Area.

The mainland and island beaches on the east coast of Peninsular Malaysia host significant populations of nesting Green Sea Turtles every year between March and August. There is also a notable population of Hawksbill Turtles that nests along Malacca's beaches, on the west coast of Peninsular Malaysia. This population has been tracked extensively and migrates from its nesting grounds in Malacca to Singapore and the Riau Island group in Indonesia. The remnants of a once-massive Leatherback Turtle rookery occasionally nest near Rantau Abang. Several Olive Ridley Turtles (*Lepidochelys olivacea*) are encountered on scattered beaches every year.

Below: The distinctive colours of the Yellowbanded Sweetlips may camouflage it when schooling in open water.

Above: Longfin Bannerfish (*Heniochus acuminatus*) are one of the most charismatic species on the reef, often found schooling above it.

Right: Mushroom corals (Fungiidae) are a family of stony corals that do not attach to the substrate. Most are a single polyp and some can change sex over the course of their lives.

Above: A female Green Sea Turtle can store the sperm of several males and use it to fertilize several clutches of eggs during a single mating season.

Left: Turtle hatcheries are commonly used to reduce threats to turtles from poaching and beach erosion. Some nests must be shaded to ensure a proper sex ratio of hatchlings since sex is determined by nest temperature.

DIVING

THERE are many options for SCUBA diving in Malaysia. Three well-known island groups on the east coast of Peninsular Malaysia have well-established facilities for diving and are all marine parks. Several other islands also offer diving facilities. Peninsular Malaysia has many islands with SCUBA-diving facilities. Among them are the Perhentian Islands near the Malaysian border with Thailand, offering white beaches and a backpacker ambiance. Further south the island groups of Redang and Tioman each feature larger islands covered by rainforest and surrounded by marine-park waters featuring rich corals and abundant fish populations. Resorts on Redang and Tioman range from high end to budget for all travellers. The nearby island of Tenggol has a few small resorts and intact reefs renowned for their diverse populations of nudibranchs.

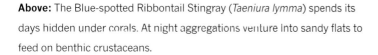

Above: The Blue-spotted Ribbontail Stingray (*Taeniura lymma*) spends its days hidden under corals. At night aggregations venture into sandy flats to feed on benthic crustaceans.

Above right: The Yellow Boxfish (*Ostracion cubicus*) can excrete a strong poison from its skin to ward off predators.

Right: The Common Lionfish (*Pterois volitans*) has become a feared and invasive species on Caribbean reefs but is a natural inhabitant of the Coral Triangle.

Scuba diving in Sabah is concentrated around Tunku Abdul Rahman Park off Kota Kinabalu, Lankayan Island in Sandakan's Sugud Islands Marine Conservation Area, and the district of Semporna. Tunku Abdul Rahman Park is Malaysia's oldest marine park and features diving close to Sabah's capital city, Kota Kinabalu. Lankayan Island, in the Sulu Sea, is accessed from the east-coast city of Sandakan and can be integrated into trips to the Turtle Islands and the Orang-utan (*Pongo pygmaeus*) rehabilitation centre at Sepilok. The resort on Lankayan enjoys exclusive access to the fully protected marine-conservation area where grouper and shark populations are rebounding after more than a decade of protection.

Bottom left: Juvenile Harlequin Sweetlips (*Plectorhinchus chaetodonoides*) wiggle to imitate a poisonous flatworm.

Bottom right: Black-tip Groupers (*Epinephelus fasciatus*) have a wide range from the Red Sea to Pitcairn Island.

Below: The Zebra Shark (*Stegostoma fasciatum*) is a nocturnal hunter on coral reefs. It is listed as Vulnerable due to overfishing.

The crown jewel of Malaysia's diving destinations is Semporna (see also page 125). Both the town and the district of that name are found in the south-east corner of Sabah abutting the Indonesian and Philippine borders. The original attraction in Semporna was Sipadan Island, made famous by Jacques Cousteau and his film of 1989, *The Ghost of the Sea Turtle*. Semporna features 50 islands ranging from those tucked deep into the well-protected Darvel Bay, to Dinawan and Si Amil, which are exposed to the power of the open Sulawesi Sea.

Semporna boasts a 70-km (43½-mile) barrier-reef formation, extensive fringing reefs, patch reefs and Malaysia's only oceanic island and pre-atoll. Sipadan is Malaysia's only island that rises from the deep sea, a seamount just 10 km (6 miles) from the edge of the continental shelf. In the middle of Semporna is the 350 sq km (135 sq mile) Tun Sakaran Marine Park. The park features eight islands, including an extinct volcanic crater that will eventually erode into an atoll. There are well-established diving resorts on Mabul, Mataking and Pom Pom islands, with many others being planned. Divers can stay at high-end resorts or budget accommodation in Semporna town itself. Besides participating in the exquisite and varied diving offered at Semporna, divers can get a glimpse of the Bajau Laut sea nomads – one of the last examples of an ancient culture that once roamed the Southeast Asian seas, with the people living their entire lives on boats.

Left: Schools of Chevron Barracuda (*Sphyraena qenie*) are a highlight of diving off Sipadan Island. Barracuda Point is one of the most famous dive sites in Malaysia.

Opposite top: Bigeye Jacks (*Caranx sexfasciatus*) form huge schools on the steep drop-offs at Sipadan Island.

Opposite below: The Titan Triggerfish (*Balistoides viridescens*) is notoriously aggressive and territorial when defending its eggs.

Right: The Giant Frogfish (*Antennarius commerson*) has an elongated first spine to its dorsal fin, which is used to attract small fish to come within striking range.

Opposite: At the foot of Bohey Dulang, Sabah Parks maintains a research lab and ranger station for the Tun Sakaran Marine Park.

Below left: Pfeffer's Flamboyant Cuttlefish (*Metasepia pfefferi*) only grow to 8 cm (3 in) in length and are the only species of cuttlefish to 'walk' along the substrate.

Below right: Pegasus sea moths (Pegasidae) have specialized mouths without teeth that are used to suck worms from their burrows on the sandy bottom.

MARINE RESOURCE MANAGEMENT

ANAGEMENT of marine resources in Malaysia differs between the states of Peninsular Malaysia, Sabah and Sarawak. Fisheries are managed in Peninsular Malaysia and Sarawak by the Federal Department of Fisheries under the Ministry of Agriculture and Agro-based Industry. Sabah has its own Department of Fisheries under its state's Ministry of Agriculture and Industrial Foods, but there is close cooperation with the federal ministry. In all three jurisdictions fisheries are managed through a system of zones extending various distances from the coast, which limit boat capacity and gear. Large commercial vessels are not allowed into coastal waters. The size of the zones varies between the federal management and Sabah. All fishing boats and gears must be licensed to operate within their respective zones, and Malaysia allows very few foreign fishing vessels into its Exclusive Economic Zone.

The use of marine protected areas for biodiversity protection is well established throughout Malaysia. The Department of Fisheries has the ability to designate 'fisheries prohibited areas', and several have been established around Peninsular Malaysia. The management of marine parks, previously under the Department of Fisheries, was moved to the Ministry of Environment and Natural Resources in 2004 and a new Department of Marine Parks was formed. This federal government agency has the ability to designate an area up to 2 km (1¼ miles) from land in Peninsular Malaysia. More than 45 islands and islets are now surrounded by such marine parks in the island groups of Perhentian, Redang and Tioman in the South China Sea, and Pulau Payar in the northern Strait of Malacca.

In Sarawak marine protected areas fall under the jurisdiction of the Sarawak Forestry Corporation. The islands of the Talatang Satang National Park are protected for the benefit of nesting Green and Hawksbill Turtles, and the Miri-Sibuti Coral Reefs National Park protects some of Sarawak's biggest coral-reef formations.

Sabah has several marine protected areas, most of which fall under the management of Sabah Parks through the Sabah Parks Enactment. One area, the Sugud Islands Marine Conservation Area, was established under the Wildlife Conservation Enactment. It is managed through a private-public partnership between the Sabah Wildlife Department, an NGO called Reef Guardian and a dive resort.

Above: Artisanal fishermen in Semporna, Sabah, come to purse-seine boats seeking unwanted fish.

Left: Growing seaweed is a popular alternative to fishing for island communities in Semporna.

Opposite: A Giant Trevally (*Caranx ignobilis*) hunts Bigeye Jacks along a wall at Sipadan Island.

THREATS *to* MARINE RESOURCES

MALAYSIA'S marine resources face a variety of threats and pressures. The main commercial fisheries employ purse-seines and bottom trawls. Fish-stock surveys by the Department of Fisheries indicate that in large areas of Malaysia stocks of bottom-dwelling demersal fish had declined by 60 to 90 per cent between the late 1960s and late '90s. The decline was most pronounced in the Strait of Malacca, an area that continues to produce more than 40 per cent of Malaysia's total fish landings annually (Ahmad, Isa, Ismail & Yusof, 2003).

LAND DEVELOPMENT

The reefs within Peninsular Malaysia's marine parks are protected from fishing. However, the land section of the islands does not fall within the park management. Thus development, particularly for tourism, is often uncontrolled. Inadequate sewerage-treatment systems and bad waste management affect the surrounding marine ecosystem, with the waters around some of the most densely populated islands showing signs of excess nutrients (Coral Triangle Initiative, 2012).

DESTRUCTIVE FISHING

In Sabah the reefs are subject to heavy fishing pressure by small-scale fishermen employing gill nets and hooks and lines. Problems with the illegal use of sodium cyanide and explosives are widespread. The demand for high-value groupers and Humphead Wrasse drives the trade for live fish. As fish populations dwindle, fishermen resort to the hazardous practice of diving with a surface-based compressor to find undersized and juvenile fish hiding among the corals. A squirt of the sodium cyanide solution stuns the fish, making it an easy catch for the diver. Often the fish will have retreated into a coral crevice and the diver must pry the corals away before he can retrieve the fish. Juvenile fish caught in this manner are kept in sea cages and fed until they reach a marketable size. To feed these captive fish, 'trash' fish is supplied through the waste from trawls or from fish caught with highly destructive home-made explosives. These bombs, made from kerosene and fertilizer, kill fish indiscriminately, and often leave craters and rubble when the detonation is too close to the bottom. Entire reefs have been blasted to rubble with this method (Coral Triangle Initiative, 2012).

TURTLE PERSECUTION

Malaysia bears the distinction of having lost one of the world's largest populations of Leatherback Turtles. Until the early 1980s hundreds of massive turtles nested every year on the 10-km (6-mile)

beach of Rantau Abang on the east coast of Peninsular Malaysia. By the mid-2000s the population was declared functionally extinct (Chan, 2006).

For more than half a century nearly every egg was collected and consumed, while adult Leatherbacks were killed by faraway hunters or caught as by-catch in long-line fisheries. Turtle eggs are now fully protected in Sabah and Sarawak. In Peninsular Malaysia it remains legal to buy and sell eggs except for Leatherback eggs in Terengganu state. In some markets, particularly in Kuala Terengganu, Green Sea Turtle and Hawksbill Turtle eggs are sold openly. The collection of turtle eggs in Peninsular Malaysia is strictly controlled through a system of licensing, and most eggs must be deposited in hatcheries. The legal sale of eggs produces an incentive for poachers and smugglers to supply a demand that is not being met by local production.

Above: Building resorts and artificial islands on the tops of coral reefs can have an impact on biodiversity and the ecological balance.

Left: Fish that cannot be sold for human consumption are sold in bulk to make fertilizer for oil-palm plantations in Sabah.

Opposite: Groupers are kept in sea cages until they reach a marketable size when they are sold to restaurants throughout East and Southeast Asia.

NATIONAL PLAN OF ACTION

MALAYSIA's National Plan of Action for the CTI was developed through a process of consultation with many stakeholders in Sabah and Peninsular Malaysia. The initial delineation of the scientific boundary of the Coral Triangle established the western edge at the same place as another multinational marine-conservation initiative, the Sulu-Sulawesi Marine Ecoregion of 2004. This is an agreement between Indonesia, Malaysia and the Philippines to conserve the marine resources of their shared seas through marine protected areas, fisheries management and endangered species protection. It is considered by many to be a precursor to the CTI (National Oceanography Directorate, 2011).

The overlap in boundaries led some in the Malaysian government to initially question the need for Malaysia to sign on to another international agreement that seemed to duplicate the previous one. When Malaysia decided to join as one of the initial six Coral Triangle countries, it was with the understanding that implementation of the agreement would be prioritized in Sabah. The coordination was managed by the National Oceanography Directorate in the Ministry of Science, Technology and Innovation, with input from the Department of Fisheries and the Ministry of Natural Resources and Environment. Sabah's Department of Fisheries and Sabah Parks, along with the Universiti Malaysia Sabah, were close and constant partners as the main agencies responsible for implementing the agreement on the ground.

The Malaysian national plan follows the Regional Plan of Action (see page 33) closely with its goals and targets. The national plan lists 133 specific actions, each with a specific output, indicators of success, a target date for completion and a list of implementing partners.

fishing vessel monitoring systems, a stronger coastguard agency, and increased awareness by enforcement officers of environmental laws and crimes.

The national plan also sets targets for improving the income and welfare of poor fishing families, as well as improving management and stocks of tuna, and targets of the live reef-fish trade. To improve management of tuna, the plan began by conducting a survey of tuna resources in Malaysian waters. The live-fish plans included a certification system for traders employing best practices when catching and trading live food fish and ornamentals.

The plan for marine protected areas, to comply with the needs for Goal 3, features actions to address marine protected areas as fisheries-management tools on coral reefs and mangroves. It includes the establishment of Malaysia's largest marine protected area, the proposed Tun Mustapha Park in northern Sabah. The plan also recognizes the need to upgrade human resources for marine protected area management, and to conduct more rigorous assessments of that management.

The action plan for Goal 4 on climate-change adaptation called for the completion of several climate-vulnerability studies in coastal areas, the development of a climate-change coastal adaptation plan and improved climate-data collection and storage. More importantly, the plan also recognizes the need to protect a wide array of habitats representative of all possible habitat types to provide healthy examples of environments that may be better able to deal with climate-change impacts. It also includes an action to reduce all non-climate related stresses, so that habitats and organisms can deal with climate-induced stresses.

The action plan for Goal 5 on conservation of threatened species includes implementing existing action plans for the management of sharks and sea turtles. It lists a need for similar plans for marine mammals, seabirds, seagrasses and invasive species.

Every goal in the national plan contains actions for planning and management, policy and administration, information and awareness, and funding. It is critical that the plan include actions related to funding. This is often overlooked when designing management plans, and activities are sometimes not conducted because of this oversight.

Under Goal 1 of the national plan (priority seascapes to be designated and effectively managed), Malaysia expressed its intention to initiate and complete physical plans for the coasts of Peninsular Malaysia and Sabah, while also conducting biodiversity and oceanographic surveys of the Strait of Malacca and South China Sea.

To achieve the plan target of having strong laws and enforcement capacity for an ecosystem approach to fisheries management, Malaysia planned on establishing an inter-agency Ecosystem Approach to Fisheries Management (EAFM) steering committee to develop a policy and to amend the Fisheries Act to include the EAFM. Coupled with the legislative plans are ambitions to improve the capacity of enforcement through increased use of

Above: Artisanal fishermen in Sabah rely on coral reefs for daily food supplies.

Opposite left: A Tomato Clownfish (*Amphiprion frenatus*) swims hard against the current to stay close to its host anemone.

Opposite right: Juveniles of the Striped Eel Catfish (*Plotosus lineatus*) form large, dense schools. Poison from the dorsal fin can be fatal.

CONSERVATION WORK

MALAYSIA has comparatively fewer conservation NGOs than the other CTI countries. Of the big international NGOs only WWF is present in Malaysia, although there are several smaller NGOs and several local ones working on marine-conservation issues.

REEF CHECK MALAYSIA

This organization is part of the global Reef Check network. Reef Check's work focuses on collecting data about coral-reef condition by training divers in a simple but robust monitoring protocol. Volunteers are trained to identify key species of fish, invertebrates and coral condition before participating in dives to monitor the health of a reef. Reef Check Malaysia conducts surveys at over 100 sites around Malaysia each year and publishes an annual report with its findings. The data is also uploaded to a global database.

Reef Check Malaysia conducts outreach programmes for schoolchildren on several islands around Peninsular Malaysia and in urban areas. This work is linked to projects that engage stakeholders and businesses on islands to improve their practices and protect the coral reefs that their livelihoods often depend upon.

TURTLE PROTECTION

Marine turtles are one of the icons of the global marine environment. Their populations declined substantially in the 20th century and have recovered in only a few locations around the world. As such, they are one of the priority species for WWF's work globally and in Malaysia. Turtles are protected by the Fisheries Act, making it a crime to harass or possess them. However, turtles are the only animal species mentioned in the Malaysian constitution, where they are put under the control of the government of each state. Therefore, when turtles are within the state boundaries, including 3 nautical miles into the sea, they are within the laws of each state (Saad, Hiew & Nagarai, 2012).

Possession of turtle eggs is banned in Sabah and Sarawak. In Peninsular Malaysia only Leatherback Turtle eggs are protected in Terengganu state. In order to fully protect turtles throughout Malaysia, laws must be passed in each state for each of the four or five species found there. Alternatively, the constitution must be changed to allow federal legislation to protect the turtles and end the threat of egg consumption. In 2009 WWF-Malaysia collected more than 100,000 signatures on a campaign for better

laws to protect turtles. Future strategies will attempt to use market forces, particularly around turtles as a draw for tourism, to generate support for comprehensive laws to protect turtles.

Critically Endangered Hawksbill Turtles nest on the beaches of Malacca state before returning to their feeding grounds around Singapore and Indonesia's Riau Archipelago. They face threats associated with living in one of the world's busiest shipping lanes, including pollution, ship strikes and loss of habitat around Singapore. When they arrive in Malacca to nest they encounter severely eroded beaches, and their eggs are collected for sale in local markets.

The state controls the collection through a system of licensing egg collectors, who must deposit the majority of collected eggs in state-run hatcheries before selling the remainder. However, the system faces abuse and poaching is a common problem. Since 2006 WWF-Malaysia has employed teams to monitor several nesting beaches along Malacca's waterfront to help collect eggs to be sent to hatcheries and to watch for poaching. An attempt has been made to include coastal resorts in the effort, and to bring value to the turtles as tourist attractions. The system of paying egg collectors is thought to be unsustainable, and WWF-Malaysia sees the need to ban egg possession and consumption altogether.

Above: Monitoring coral reefs requires intense data collection for tracking coral cover, fish populations and other organisms.

Opposite: Sipadan Island is renowned for its large populations of Green Sea Turtles.

FISH PROTECTION

As Malaysia continues to grow in affluence, consumers will have increasing power to influence how resources are managed and exploited. Shark Savers Malaysia, a branch of the global Shark Savers network, launched an 'I'm FINished with fins' campaign in 2014 to reduce demand for shark's fin soup in Malaysia. Celebrities from around Malaysia signed up to pledge their support for the campaign and to encourage the public in Malaysia to stop eating the soup that drives much of the overfishing of sharks.

WWF-Malaysia maintains a database of Malaysian fisheries and employs a robust system of ranking each fishery according to its sustainability. The resulting guide gives consumers the power to pick fish that are better for the environment and helps to spread the word about sustainable fisheries (WWF-Malaysia, n.d.).

MARINE PROTECTED AREAS

In 2001 a group of more than 100 scientists and conservationists with international, regional and local expertise developed a vision for the Sulu-Sulawesi Marine Ecoregion and identified priority areas for conservation. That vision became the foundation for the tri-national conservation plan agreed upon by the governments of Indonesia, Malaysia and the Philippines.

THE PROPOSED TUN MUSTAPHA PARK

The Sabah state government shortly thereafter declared its intention to establish Malaysia's largest marine protected area in one of those sites, the Kudat-Banggi Priority Conservation Area. Located at the northern tip of Borneo, the conservation area separates the Sulu Sea from the South China Sea, and forms the southern edge of the Balabac Strait separating Borneo from the Philippine island of Palawan. It was described as a globally important conservation area for its rich mix of corals, mangroves and seagrasses, located in the heart of the world's pinnacle of marine biodiversity. The proposed boundary would include nearly all the waters of three districts (Kota Marudu, Kudat and Pitas), encompass nearly 50 islands and protect Malaysia's second biggest concentration of coral reefs. At 1.02 million ha (2.5 million acres), it would also be one of Southeast Asia's largest marine protected areas.

Such a large marine protected area was unprecedented in Malaysia. At the time of its proposal no marine protected area had ever included local communities living within its boundaries, and the proposed Tun Mustapha Park could include more than 80,000 people, and incorporate significant subsistence and commercial fisheries. Subsequent to the announcement, the Tun Sakaran Marine Park (see page 127) was gazetted in Semporna. The Semporna park became the first to include local communities, but at a much smaller scale, with only several thousand people and one-third the size of the Kudat-Banggi Priority Conservation Area.

WWF-Malaysia and Universiti Malaysia Sabah became key partners to the state government to help establish the proposed Tun Mustapha Park, but the initial challenges were immense. Commercial fishermen were afraid of losing their livelihoods, and communities on the islands had no concept of community-based management or conservation. They were among the poorest communities in Malaysia. WWF-Malaysia partnered with Sabah Parks to begin awareness campaigns about marine resources, marine-resource management and the role of marine protected areas in maintaining fisheries. At the same time it conducted socio-economic and marine-habitat surveys to better understand the remote parts of the proposed park. An environmental-awareness centre was established on the largest island, Banggi, and a group of the local youth was trained to become environmental champions. Several communities around the park were enlisted to create demonstration sites for locally managed marine protected areas. More communities soon volunteered to also try and establish similar efforts in their areas.

WWF-Malaysia made contact with the commercial fishermen of Kudat, the main fishing port of the park. The fishermen agreed that something needed to change as catches were dwindling and competition was growing ever more fierce. They saw the park as an opportunity to give more input into the management of their marine resources, and formed a new advocacy group of commercial fishing boat owners. The members asked for more information about ecosystem approaches to fisheries management, monitoring fishing efforts and marine ecology. That group soon grew into one of the key advocates for the Tun Mustapha Park.

The Tun Mustapha Park is changing the paradigm of marine protected area management in Malaysia. Besides bringing local communities and commercial fisheries into the process for management, it also requires intensive collaboration between government offices that rarely work closely together. A committee of more than 25 agencies was established in 2011 with the mandate of drafting a management plan. Including a system of zones for various uses, this will be opened to a six-month public comment period with a target to gazette the park by 2015.

During the nearly ten-year process towards the establishment of the park, small achievements have pointed towards major changes in thinking. A survey of Dugongs around Pulau Banggi in 2004 gathered stories from local communities about the best ways to cook the animals and how to make love potions from their tears. In 2009, when a baby Dugong was found in the net of a fisherman at one of the demonstration sites, a discussion ensued about what to do with the animal. Some community members advocated killing and eating it, some proposed keeping it as a tourist attraction and some argued that it should be released. In the end the baby was

released and not seen again. This small win indicated that a corner had been turned and that the local mindsets had changed, giving hope for the future of the Tun Mustapha Park.

SEMPORNA

Another globally important conservation priority was identified around Semporna, at Sabah's south-east corner facing the Sulawesi Sea. The waters around Semporna include Malaysia's largest concentration of coral reefs and perhaps its highest coral and fish richness. Semporna's 50 islands and mainland coastline offer many ecological niches, each colonized by a slightly different complex of organisms. The outer islands of Si Amil, Mataking and Pom Pom are far away from the influences of the Borneo mainland, and the waters are generally clear. Closer to land there are complexes of mangroves interspersed with unusual corals.

Most of the islands in Semporna have some communities living on them. The people are usually fishing families, although some have adopted seaweed farming either as full-time or part-time livelihoods. Semporna has a close cultural connection with the neighbouring Sulu Archipelago of the Philippines, dating back to the times when the Sultan of Sulu ruled most of north-eastern Borneo. The connections remain, with many families on islands in Semporna having migrated to Semporna as refugees from the conflicts against the Philippine government in the 1970s and '80s, as illegal immigrants or as migrant workers. In most cases they are entirely dependent upon the sea. One of the last groups of Bajau Laut sea nomads uses Semporna as a traditional fishing ground as it moves between the Sulu Archipelago and eastern Sabah, maintaining a lifestyle little changed over the centuries. Many of these people are stateless and rarely venture onto land.

Juxtaposed with these local communities, which are entirely dependent on the sea and live in relative poverty, is Semporna's lucrative and thriving SCUBA diving and tourism industry. The first diving resorts were concentrated on Sipadan Island in the

Above: Whitetip Reef Sharks (*Triaenodon obesus*) spend most of the day resting on the reef bottom or in a cave. At night they emerge to hunt fish and octopus, often in groups.

1980s and '90s. Increasing pressure on the small island forced the Malaysian government to close all the resorts on the island in 2004 in an effort to protect the fragile topside and underwater environment. Most of the resorts moved to neighbouring Mabul Island, and more resorts popped up on several surrounding islands, as well as in Semporna town on the mainland. Some of the islands are overcrowded and lack basic sanitation facilities. Balancing the needs of the local communities with the desires of the diving industry, along with the ecological constraints of the fragile ecosystem, make conservation in Semporna particularly challenging. Semporna's lack of a development plan and comprehensive zoning plan result in frequent conflicts between users.

There is also a problem with destructive fishing and overfishing in Semporna. Some communities made extensive use of blast fishing in the past and the practice continues. Fishermen use home-made explosive devices, usually fashioned from a bottle, some fertilizer, kerosene and a detonator, to target schools of fish. Fusiliers were common targets as they usually school in shallow areas close to reef slopes. The fishermen generally cruise around the reef edge looking through the clear waters for a school of fish before throwing the bomb. The shockwave from the explosion kills many fish and the fisherman can simply collect them from the surface or free dive to collect those

that have sunk. The detonators are primitive and there is no way to precisely time when a bomb explodes. Sometimes it explodes before it is cast, maiming or killing the fishermen. Sometimes it takes too long to explode and only detonates when close to or on the corals. These late explosions destroy vast areas of coral reef.

A consortium of NGOs, led by the Maine Conservation Society, spent nearly 20 years working in Semporna to establish the Tun Sakaran Marine Park. Originally proposed to be called the Semporna Islands Park, it was eventually gazetted in 2004. The objectives of the park are to protect the natural environment on land and in the sea, and to promote sustainable use of natural resources by its 3,000 inhabitants. The Maine Conservation Society-UK continues to work with Sabah Parks on a zoning plan allocating areas inside the park where fishing is allowed by the local communities, and where they can farm and harvest seaweed, and areas that will be designated as off limits to any form of fishing.

Opposite: Yellowfin Goatfish (*Mulloidichthys vanicolensus*) school during the day for protection and hunt for crustaceans in the sand at night.

Below: Tourist resorts in Semporna can help combat poverty and fish bombing but can also bring unsustainable development.

Of critical importance is the complex task of determining who counts as a member of the local community and who does not. The nomadic Bajau Laut have used the islands around the park for decades but do not reside there permanently. Many people living on the mainland in Semporna or as far away as Kuala Lumpur make claims as natives of the islands.

The Maine Conservation Society and Sabah Parks have a constant task to raise awareness about the park and its regulations. One of the key functions is to eliminate blast fishing in the park, but Sabah Parks struggles to find resources to conduct regular patrols and enforcement.

Fish bombing is a particularly difficult problem to solve in Semporna. During a 2011 regional symposium on combating blast fishing, Malaysian authorities requested more reports of fish bombing to use when making requests for additional resources to patrol and enforce the seas around Semporna. Reef Check Malaysia took up the cause and established a fish-bomb reporting system where reports can be submitted via mobile phone or the internet detailing the date, location and time of an incident. Between 2011 and 2013 more than 100 reports were collected and submitted to the authorities (Reef Check Malaysia, 2014).

Sustainable management of marine resources in Semporna aims to conserve the outstanding marine biodiversity while allowing it to support the lives and livelihoods of local communities. Marine protected areas can preserve critical areas and promote fish production by conserving breeding adults. Mangrove habitats for juvenile fish and invertebrates like shrimp and crab are protected as well. The marine protected areas can also help to restore coral reefs and fish populations that attract SCUBA divers. However, if this comes at the cost of local communities losing access to fishing ground, the prospects for success are limited.

After several years of working with local communities around Semporna to build awareness about marine conservation and resource management, as well as working with government and the tourism sector, WWF-Malaysia is engaging in a process of establishing a zoning plan in Semporna that will be the product of extensive consultation and setting of targets for management. The establishment of zones will reduce conflict between resource users and promote sustainability.

Above: A small bridge linking two communities in Semporna also carries electricity between the islands.

Opposite: The sharp beak of the Bumphead Parrotfish (*Bolbometopon muricatum*) is used to scrape live corals off the rocky skeleton.

5
PAPUA NEW GUINEA

Papua New Guinea occupies the eastern half of New Guinea, the world's second biggest island, the Bismarck Archipelago to the north, and Bougainville Island in the Solomon Islands chain, among numerous other islands and reefs. Its 460,000 sq km (177,600 sq mile) land area is surrounded by 3.12 million sq km (1.24 sq miles) of seas, comprising the Pacific Ocean, Bismarck, Solomon, Arafura and Coral Seas, Gulf of Papua and Torres Strait.

Left: The deep red colour of the Pinjalo Snapper (*Pinjalo pinjalo*) may help to make it invisible to predators at depth.

PAPUA NEW GUINEA

Map labels:
ADMIRALTY ISLANDS — Manus Island — Lorengau — Mussau Island — Tigak Archipelago — New Hanover — Nago — Kavieng — Kavieng Lagoon — Djaul — Tabar Island — Bismarck Archipelago — New Ireland — Sepik River — BISMARCK SEA — Witu Islands — Tanga Island — Rabaul — Green Island — EAST NEW BRITAIN — BISMARCK RANGE — Madang Lagoon — Madang — Kimbe Bay — Buka — Mount Hagen — Goroka — Kimbe — New Britain — Buganville — Arawa — Huon Peninsula — Kandrian — WEST NEW BRITAIN — SOUTHERN HIGHLANDS — EASTERN HIGHLANDS — Lae — P A P U A   N E W   G U I N E A — Huon Gulf — Kikori — S O L O M O N   S E A — Fly River — Gulf of Papua — Kiriwina — Woodlark Island — Tufi — Goodenough Island — PORT MORESBY — Fergusson Island — D'ENTRECASTEAUX ISLANDS — Torres Strait — Normanby Island — Alotau — Milne Bay — Misima Island — Conflict Group — Cape York Peninsula — A U S T R A L I A — Tagula Island — INDONESIA

Legend:
200m
2000m
4000m
Coral reefs
Towns/cities

Scale:
0 — 200 Miles
0 — 300 Kilometres

A central spine of high mountains that reach more than 4,000 m (13,125 ft) above sea level dominates the mainland, and several large rivers drain the steep mountains to the north and south. Papua New Guinea's only land border splits New Guinea with Indonesia, Australia lies south across the Torres Strait and the Solomon Islands lies to the east of Bougainville. The Bismarck Archipelago includes several very large islands, such as New Britain, New Ireland and Manus, plus a constellation of smaller islands. The country is part of the Pacific Ring of Fire, experiences frequent earthquakes and has several active volcanoes.

To the south of Papua New Guinea is the Gulf of Papua; the island's largest rivers, such as the Fly and Turama, drain into the gulf, which contains vast mangrove forests. This area is thought to be home to one of the biggest remaining populations of Dugongs in the world. The extensive reef formations of the Torres Strait, part of Australia, nearly reach the southern coast of Papua New Guinea. The eastern portion of the south coast features a barrier reef formation that stretches for more than 500 km (310 miles). On the north coast fringing reefs dominate, except where several large rivers (including the Sepik and Markham) bring excessive fresh water and sediment that prevent coral growth.

The island of New Britain forms the boundary between the Bismarck and Solomon Seas. Similarly, New Ireland separates these two seas from the Pacific Ocean to the north. Both islands are surrounded by fringing and patch reefs, as is Manus Island. Several large atolls are located in the Bismarck Sea west of Manus. The reefs around Bougainville Island are largely unknown and unstudied.

Papua New Guinea's largest complex of reefs is located off the south-east tip of the mainland around Milne Bay and the Trobiand Islands. Milne Bay province alone may have more than 30 per cent of Papua New Guinea's coral reefs. The vast reefs of the Louisiade Archipelago feature several well-developed barrier reef systems, including the 640 km (400 mile) long Calvados Barrier Reef. To the north of New Ireland and Bougainville Islands there are several remote islands and atolls, including massive Lyra Reef atoll. Estimates of Papua New Guinea's reef area vary between 13,840 sq km (5,345 sq miles) and 40,000 sq km (15,445 sq miles), giving an idea of how poorly known and documented the reefs are.

Above: The harbour of Rabaul was once a huge volcano. Now several small volcanoes remain active around its former rim.

Left: Many of Papua New Guinea's coral reefs remain in excellent condition, in part due to the relatively small human population.

Above: The tropical fjords of Tufi are an unusual habitat for corals and may harbour species not found in other locations.

Right: Yellowstripe Scad (*Selaroides leptolepis*) are an important food source for many coastal communities in the Coral Triangle.

Above: Schools of Redbelly Yellowtail Fusiliers (*Caesio cuning*) hunt for plankton in the currents above a coral reef.

Left: The Blue Razorfish (*Xyrichtys pavo*) uses its elongated dorsal spine to imitate a drifting leaf.

The PEOPLE

APUA New Guinea has a population of 6.4 million people, of whom only 13 per cent live within urban areas. Many communities lack basic services and electricity supplies. The population is extremely heterogeneous, and more than 800 distinct languages are spoken throughout the country, many of which have fewer than 1,000 speakers. It is estimated that slightly more than 62 per cent of people over the age of 15 can read and write, and men have a distinctly higher literacy rate than women. The gross domestic product per capita is only US $2,800 per year.

Most people in Papua New Guinea depend on their home gardens, growing bananas, coconuts and root crops for their basic nutritional needs. In coastal areas artisanal fishing and the collection of invertebrates supplements the provisions of gardens. Throughout Papua New Guinea the land, and access to land, is governed through a complex system of traditional tenure and management passed through family groups or clans, as is common in much of Melanesia. This system often extends to marine resources and reef areas.

Above right: A traditional house in West New Britain province.

Right: Children learn the techniques of the single outrigger canoe at a young age.

LOCAL IMPACTS *on* REEFS

COMMUNITIES have access to the reefs near their home villages, and access to these reefs by outsiders usually requires permission from the local chief or landowner.

TRADITIONAL MANAGEMENT

Traditional forms of marine-resource management included setting up 'taboo' areas at certain times, when access to fishing or the collection of shellfish was prohibited. Often a taboo area was set in anticipation of a feast for a special event, and the area was opened to fishing just before the event. The closure of the area would have allowed fish and shellfish to accumulate and grow bigger. This system of ownership works well in areas with relatively small populations and strong traditional leadership. However, as Papua New Guinea has started to move into a cash economy and migration to earn cash has increased, there have been a growing number of conflicts over access to land and fishing resources.

LAND-BASED IMPACTS

It is often stated that Papua New Guinea's marine resources, particularly the coral reefs and mangroves, are less impacted than those of neighbouring countries in Southeast Asia and the Pacific Islands. While this may be true in many areas, there are examples throughout the country of places where marine resources have been locally over exploited or degraded through land-based activities.

Several large mines in Papua New Guinea are known to have dumped tailings into neighbouring rivers and coastal areas, in some cases leading to the smothering of large areas of fringing reef. Extensive areas of logging, even on relatively small islands, have impacted coastal resources through increased sedimentation.

Increasingly large areas are being planted for oil palm, attracting migrants from other regions to supply labour to the plantations. Clearing land for new plantings and the gardens that new settlers plant can all lead to increased sedimentation. Some areas with growing populations also experience decreasing near-shore fish populations and reef health.

EFFECTS OF FISHING

Fisheries are managed by the National Fisheries Authority, but much of the power for local implementation is devolved to local-level governments, and implementation of coastal management depends on their will and capacity (see also page 138).

Left: Oil-palm planting, logging and mining are some of the land-based activities that may have an impact on coastal water quality in parts of Papua New Guinea.

Papua New Guinea is one of the world's largest producers of tuna in the world. In 2007 the national and foreign fleet of tuna purse-seiners landed 256,000 tons of tuna worth nearly US $345 million. It is estimated that the catch increased to 702,000 tons by 2010. A smaller hand-line fishery targets sashimi-grade tuna. There are also extensive shrimp-trawl fisheries along the southern coasts of mainland Papua New Guinea.

The purse-seines primarily land Skipjack Tuna along with some Yellow Fin Tuna. In 2012 the Skipjack fisheries from the countries of the Parties to the Nauru Agreement (Federated States of Micronesia, Kiribati, Marshall Islands, Nauru, Palau, Papua New Guinea, Solomon Islands and Tuvalu) achieved Marine Stewardship Council certification as a sustainable fishery. The products, all caught with purse-seine gear and without the use of fish-aggregating devices, are now marketed via a single company called Pacifical. Papua New Guinea has mandated that all boats landing Skipjack Tuna in the country must land Marine Stewardship Council certified catch as of 2013. This overcomes problems related to keeping fish caught with sustainable methods separate from those caught with unsustainable methods. It was found that many of the fishing boats and processing areas lacked sufficient capacity to separate the certified and uncertified fish.

Coastal fisheries in Papua New Guinea are mostly for local consumption of fish and shellfish. However, some invertebrates, particularly sea cucumbers and some shell species, such as trochus shells, which are used in making buttons and other ornamental objects, are collected and sold on a commercial basis.

Sea cucumbers are dried and traded primarily to Southeast Asian and East Asian markets. The most prized species can fetch up to US $120 for 1 kg (2¼ lb). Chinese traders first started coming to Papua New Guinea's Milne Bay Province to trade for sea cucumbers, among other sea products, at the end of the 19th century. The trade intensified in the 1970s and boomed in the '90s, until stocks throughout Papua New Guinea were depleted.

For many coastal communities the sea-cucumber trade was one of their only sources of cash, and the depletion led to hardships. By 2009 the situation had become even worse and the Papua New Guinea government banned all sea-cucumber fishing for three years, and extended the ban for another three years in 2012. The ban supplements a management plan that had guidelines for gear and size limits which had been in place since the mid-1990s, but was ineffective. With the ban in place populations should rebound if poaching levels are kept to a minimum and if there were adequate adult sea cucumbers remaining for reproduction.

Most coastal communities rely on local reefs and mangroves for their daily protein needs. There are very few studies on the status of near-shore marine resources throughout Papua New Guinea, but some have been conducted in limited areas. The National Fisheries Authority has set restrictions on gear and size limits for some species, but efforts to monitor and control fisheries at the local level are hampered by the highly dispersed nature of the coastal communities, with many in remote areas rarely getting visits from government officers (Cinner, 2006).

Most local communities fish with hook and line, gill nets or spear guns. In some areas the use of illegal poisonous derris root and dynamite is also an issue. In Kimbe Bay there is no fish market in the town and fishermen generally sell their excess fish within the community itself. The local government is hoping to develop ice-making facilities and a system for fishermen to preserve their fish long enough to bring it to market. It aspires to developing a market for fish, and this will give the reef more value to the communities, which will then be earning more cash from the resource and have an incentive to protect it.

Above: Papua New Guinea, along with the Solomon Islands, banned the collection of sea cucumbers for several years because of crashing populations.

Opposite: Soft corals do not build stony skeletons but have calcareous spicules in their tissues to give them support.

CONSERVATION CHALLENGES

PAPUA New Guinea is a biodiversity hotspot on land and in the sea. It has been listed as a 'true wilderness' area, as a WWF 'Global 200 Ecoregion' and as one of 12 'megadiverse' countries. As such, it has long been a top-priority country for most of the big international NGOs, including WWF, TNC, Conservation International and WCS. Unfortunately, conservation in the country has had a chequered history.

One of the biggest challenges is the mismatch between some of the most commonly used conservation tools, protected areas and the extremely high rate of land ownership. With 85–95 per cent of the country's land and seas under family and clan traditional ownership and management, it is nearly impossible for the government to designate and manage any large protected areas or national parks in their traditional Western format. Local communities, which rely on access to the land and sea for their livelihoods, require some form of compensation for relinquishing access to those resources. In some cases, conservation becomes a commodity that the communities attempt to trade or barter for development aid (Melick, Kinch & Govan, 2012).

In the 1990s and early 2000s the concept of 'integrated conservation and development' dominated conservation approaches in the Melanesia region. However, it was observed that organizations implementing programmes primarily to save biodiversity were not well versed at providing development projects, and the promised development aspects of the projects were often not delivered or inappropriate for the community in question. This led to communities distrusting the motivations and promises of those aiming to protect biodiversity (Foale, 2001).

Today, the approach tends to fall more within the bounds of sustainable development, and building on aspects of traditional tenure and management. However, over the years a certain amount of distrust has built up towards large conservation programmes. One problem is that the national government has signed several international agreements, including the Convention on Biological Diversity and the CTI Regional Plan of Action (see page 140), which set ambitious targets for the area of the country that should be under protected areas. It has been noted that the current land-ownership issues and capacity of the national government will be major hindrances to meeting those targets (Melick et al., 2012).

NATIONAL PLAN *of* ACTION

PAPUA New Guinea's CTI National Plan of Action is designed to address several identified threats.

- Excessive direct take due to the overharvesting of marine resources for commercial or subsistence purposes, and also relating to by-catch issues in several fisheries.
- The potential of climate change to impact all of Papua New Guinea's marine resources through increased seawater temperatures, changes in salinity from altered rainfall patterns and increased acidity of seawater.
- Habitat destruction from some coastal development, sedimentation and nutrient input from land-use practices and other habitat impacts.
- Logging, mining and large-scale agriculture all have the biggest impacts on marine habitats through increased sediment inputs.
- Pollution, on top of the land-based inputs, from some urban areas and industrial operations.

The national plan's organizing principle is that all actions will reduce threats, while ensuring 'that management of marine resources must be for creation of jobs [and] economic growth' to reduce poverty and increase food security. Environmental sustainability is enshrined in the national constitution through Goal 4 and the directive principle, which states that 'Papua New Guinea's natural resource and environment [are] to be conserved and used for the collective benefit for us all, and to be replenished for the future generations'. The national plan in Papua New Guinea is led by the Department of Environmental Conservation and the National Fisheries Authority. It replicates the regional plan's goals:

1. Designating and effectively managing 'priority seascapes'.
2. Fully applying an ecosystem approach to fisheries management and other marine resources.
3. Establishing and effectively managing marine protected areas.
4. Achieving climate-change adaptation measures.
5. Improving the status of threatened species.

Specific activities within each goal are unique to Papua New Guinea.

Papua New Guinea, along with Indonesia and the Solomon Islands, completed an ecoregional vision for the Bismarck Solomon Seas Ecoregion in 2003. The plan identified important areas for conservation and an agreement for the conservation of Leatherback Turtles (*Dermachelys coriacea*) – an iconic species of the Pacific still found nesting in all three jurisdictions of the ecoregion.

Activities identified for Goal 1 included policy reviews to better integrate government agencies for marine management, developing investment plans for ecoregion conservation and identifying other important areas for conservation. This includes outlining customary ownership rules and user rules for marine resources.

Goal 2 states that the ecosystem approach to fisheries management fits Papua New Guinea better than conventional fisheries management because of its emphasis on humans as part of the ecosystem, area management, community management and user rights. Specific actions include incorporating the ecosystem approach into the national Fisheries Act of 2000, strengthening the decentralization of coastal fisheries management, and increasing enforcement capacity at provincial and local levels. Reinvigorating the National Fisheries College and a National Mariculture Research Centre, both in Kavieng, are also on the list.

Goal 3 is establishing and effectively managing marine protected areas. Such areas are not clearly defined in any of Papua New Guinea's legislation, but the term has been applied to a wide spectrum of areas that are subject to some protection of natural and cultural marine regions. Specific activities include creating appropriate policies that will help to develop networks of marine protected areas, with an emphasis on the locally managed marine area model. Also part of the activities is engaging more communities and the tourism sector in protecting coastal resources, and producing management plans for existing and new areas.

Adaptation to climate change is Goal 4. Actions for priority implementation include basic activities such as conducting vulnerability assessments, raising awareness about the threats of climate change, protection of coral reefs and finding ways to build climate-change resilience into national development policies.

Papua New Guinea is home to many endangered species, including Sperm Whales, Orcas (*Orcinus orca*) and many dolphin species, Leatherback Turtles and one of the world's biggest remaining populations of Dugongs. Actions for endangered species conservation in the national plan, Goal 5, include assessing the status of endangered species in the country, and building capacity at the provincial and local levels to manage endangered species.

Opposite: The Pink Anemonefish (*Amphiprion perideraion*) is a sequential hermaphrodite. When the female dies, the largest male of the family group will gain weight and change sex to become the breeding female.

NON-GOVERNMENT INITIATIVES

BESIDES the government agencies responsible for the management of marine resources and conservation, there are several international and local NGOs working to save the Coral Triangle in Papua New Guinea. TNC, Conservation International, WWF and WCS are all active in the country, and running marine-conservation projects. The Locally Managed Marine Area network is also active in Papua New Guinea, helping to establish coastal conservation areas. The main priority areas for the international NGOs include Kimbe Bay on New Britain, the islands around Kavieng in New Ireland province, Madang Lagoon on the mainland's north coast and the coral reef-rich province of Milne Bay. Conservation work in the first two of these areas is highlighted below.

KIMBE BAY

The story of marine conservation in Kimbe Bay starts with a young Australian oil-palm planter in 1966. Shortly after first visiting Kimbe as an Australian government agricultural extension worker, Max Benjamin bought the Walindi Plantation along the coast and eventually started exploring the seas in his free time. However, he and his wife Cecile did not realize the value of their backyard reefs until they took a dive trip to the Red Sea.

The Red Sea was the premier diving destination at the time, and Max and Cecile quickly realized that their reefs in Kimbe Bay were richer and in better condition. Over the years more and more visitors came to the Walindi Plantation when they heard that Max and Cecile had a compressor, and the Walindi Plantation Resort was born. Eventually Cecile gave some presentations at the University of Papua New Guinea and in New Zealand, which attracted the attention of the European Union and TNC.

A deal with the European Union resulted in the construction of the Kimbe Bay Marine Research Centre on plantation land donated by Max and Cecile. TNC was invited to the area by the owners of the Walindi Plantation Resort to help install boat moorings on dive sites in order to prevent anchor damage from the increasing SCUBA divers. TNC established an office and began conducting marine surveys of the biodiversity and health of the coral reefs. In 1994 it led the first of a series of Rapid Ecological Assessments of corals, fish, seagrasses, mangroves and cetaceans, which identified Kimbe Bay as a real biodiversity treasure.

Kimbe Bay is unusual in Papua New Guinea because a large proportion of its residents have only a loose connection to the sea. Many of the settlers in Kimbe migrated from the New Guinea highlands to work on the oil-palm plantations, and do not have a traditional knowledge of the sea. Within only 50 km (31 miles) of Kimbe Bay, the local communities are expert seafarers and fishermen, but they do not access the reefs of Kimbe Bay.

Right: Grey Reef Sharks (*Carcharhinus amblyrhynchos*) can be common on reefs in Papua New Guinea.

Opposite: At Kimbe Bay, the Walindi Plantation Resort installed mooring buoys so that dive boats do not need to anchor on the reef, thus minimizing damage to corals.

Above: Gorgonian sea fans stretch along the top of a coral ridge to catch plankton from the currents.

Right: Clown Triggerfish (*Balistoides conspicillum*) are highly territorial and aggressive towards other fish.

Above: Grey Reef Sharks can live for up to 25 years and have been observed herding prey against a reef wall to make it easier to catch.

Left: The Red-spotted Box Crab (*Calappa calappa*) is active at night and feeds on clams. It can prise them open or crack the shell with its strong pincers.

The need for more awareness of the importance of the sea and how to manage it was obvious. Dovetailing with Max and Cecile Benjamin's vision that Papua New Guinea needed education and healthcare more than anything else, TNC helped to establish a local NGO called Mahonia Na Dari ('Guardians of the Sea' in the local language of the Talasea Peninsula).

Mahonia Na Dari's mission is to understand and conserve the natural environments of Kimbe Bay and Papua New Guinea for the benefit of current and future generations. Since being incorporated in 1998 as a local NGO, Mahonia Na Dari has run its marine environmental educational programmes for tens of thousands of primary and secondary students from around Kimbe Bay. It also worked with TNC to conduct outreach programmes with local communities to raise awareness about marine-resource management and the role of protected areas.

As TNC worked with Mahonia Na Dari and others to set up more and more locally managed marine areas with coastal communities around the bay, it became clear that a new strategy was needed to confront the threats facing the area. While overfishing and destructive fishing were not yet acute threats, there was some localized overfishing and some continued use of a local plant, derris root, to poison fish on the reef. The impacts of sedimentation and pollution from the growing human population, the on-going logging and the large-scale agriculture, mostly oil palm, were causes for greater concern. When coupled with the spectre of climate-change impacts, it was clear that a more thorough approach was needed.

TNC decided that Kimbe Bay was an ideal place in which to test emerging science for designing a network of marine protected areas that would be resilient to the impacts of climate change (Green et al., 2007). At the time, the best science suggested that a network of marine protected areas could be more resilient to climate-change impacts if it represented all habitats in replication, protected special and unique areas, sites connected via currents and movement of organisms, was well managed and took into account socioeconomic needs and principles. Upon adopting these principles, TNC took on a four-year project that eventually identified 15 areas of interest which, if protected, would represent a system of areas that are connected via ocean currents and share enough coral and fish larvae to repopulate each other in the event of a catastrophic coral die-off.

It took three major scientific workshops, two years of additional environmental and socioeconomic surveys, and the application of sophisticated mapping and decision-support software to produce the network. TNC, along with relevant stakeholders, decided on a set of 51 total targets (habitats or species), which had to be met by the network while minimizing the impact to local users in terms of lost fishing opportunity. They attempted to have 20 per cent of each target in the network, except for seamounts and grouper spawning aggregation sites, which needed 100 per cent coverage.

Marxan software (conservation planning software) evaluates millions of permutations and configurations of a potential protected area network, and eventually produces several options that meet the criteria and keep the impacts on local communities below a minimum threshold. However, the software only gives decision makers options from which to choose. Once the final map was produced, the hard work of getting local communities to protect each of the 15 identified areas would have to start. Unfortunately, as is often the case, other forces conspired to make TNC leave Kimbe Bay before the network could be implemented.

Manhonia Na Dari keeps up the work of pursuing the locally managed marine areas along with another group of community leaders called HOBITA (which stands for the three main communities: Hoskins, Bialla and Talasea). Besides running nine-week marine-education programmes for three high schools around Kimbe Bay, and conducting teacher training throughout Papua New Guinea, Mahonia Na Dari employs staff who conduct regular activities with coastal communities to raise awareness about how to develop and implement a coastal management plan on clan reefs. Despite having the support of the Walindi Plantation Resort and an ongoing relationship with Australia's James Cook University, Mahonia Na Dari struggles to find adequate funding and can only work with communities when funds allow.

Above: The High-fin Coral Grouper (*Plectropomus oligacanthus*) is generally rare within its range and considered Near Threatened because of overfishing for the live reef-fish trade.

Opposite: Sunset behind one of the islands near Kavieng. With a large lagoon, mangroves and open sea reefs, Kavieng has high biodiversity.

KAVIENG LAGOON

Another high-priority area for marine conservation in Papua New Guinea lies at the eastern end of New Ireland Island, including New Hannover Island and the Tigak archipelago between the two. The islands separate the Bismarck Sea from the expanse of the Pacific Ocean to the north. A Rapid Environmental Assessment survey conducted by TNC in 2006 (Hamilton, Green & Almany, 2009) found eastern New Ireland and neighbouring Manus Island to have very high concentrations of fish and coral species, befitting their inclusion within the Coral Triangle. The Tigak Islands recorded 408 coral species and 801 fish species (including Manus). It is suspected that the Kavieng Lagoon hosts rich biodiversity in many other taxa as well, as would be expected of a seascape with so many habitat types, and a major expedition of 30 scientists will spend 30 days in 2014 examining the area in great detail.

WCS, a US-based environmental NGO, has an office in Kavieng that focuses on marine-resource management in the area. There is an award-winning local NGO called Ailan Awareness that works with local communities to manage coastal resources (see page 148), and the local surfer resorts also contribute to conservation. TNC also maintains one officer in Kavieng. These NGOs are explicit partners with the New Ireland Provincial Division of Fisheries and Marine Resources, as stated in the province's marine

resource strategy. The provincial government includes NGOs as key partners in helping communities to establish locally managed marine areas and to help conduct outreach to far-flung villages.

WCS, based in New York City, is associated with the Bronx Zoo, and has a mission to save wildlife and wild places across the globe. In Papua New Guinea, it has realized that the failures of previous approaches to marine conservation were due to not adequately responding to the existing social, cultural and governance realities. This resulted in many years of wasted opportunities and funds, with local communities often losing trust in the conservation initiatives and organizations that had descended upon them. Trust was often lost through unrealized expectations of the communities when the conservation organizations promised lofty results or unintentionally created expectations by bringing large budgets into an area.

After many years of ecological and social research in the country, WCS developed a new strategy that is built on the existing governance structure of Papua New Guinea. Building on the national legislative framework that supports community management of resources, WCS has a strategy of working closely with local communities via their local-level government units, and it set a goal that aimed for the support of local livelihoods by marine and terrestrial ecosystems.

WCS identified that well-functioning community resource-management systems, local leaders who advocate for their communities' needs and a good system of government-service delivery were all key aspects of success. To achieve this it developed a strategy that it feels is scalable throughout Papua New Guinea's coastal areas. It involves being invited into local communities, building resource-management plans with communities and getting government support for the plans through the existing structures of the local-level government. Supplementing this strategy is building capacity at provincial levels of government and with local scientists.

In Kavieng, WCS is attempting to work with eight communities. For an office that only has a handful of staff, including one community-engagement specialist, this can be a major challenge. In order to avoid the common trap of not meeting community expectations, WCS follows an explicit community-engagement strategy which includes a requirement that WCS must receive a written invitation from the community before it will enter a village and conduct talks, field trips, and workshops to raise awareness about the environment and environmental issues. The next step is to find out the aspirations of the community. Once WCS has an agreement with the community, it begins a process of identifying problems with marine resources and planning actions to manage them. WCS also makes it clear that it is not a donor agency, and will not give cash or other goods to the communities.

In Kavieng, to help the sole community-engagement officer WCS recruited ten community facilitators from around the area. They work for WCS on a part-time basis and receive training in communications, work planning, climate change and marine-resource management, before practising their new skills in field trips. When WCS goes to work with communities, it usually takes five facilitators for up to two weeks into a village. This can be a challenge for female facilitators, who face pressure when leaving their families for more than a few days. Of the ten facilitators recruited in 2013, WCS had already lost the only two female ones by the beginning of 2014.

A typical management plan, like that produced for Ungakum village, is a simple 20-page document that outlines the main resources and threats in an area, as well as management actions and a monitoring plan. In Ungakum the community identified eight key resources, including mangroves, parrotfish, mud crabs and trochus shells. It then delineated a taboo zone that would be off limits to all fishing, and minimum sizes for harvesting trees, mud crabs and sea cucumbers. It prohibited fishing when fish were gathering for spawning, and taking fish that were obviously developing eggs, and restricted the minimum mesh size of fishing nets on reefs. All of these measures are designed to meet the goals of improving fishing and restoring depleted marine resources.

AILAN AWARENESS

WCS is fortunate in having a strong local NGO to work with around the region. Ailan Awareness (Island Awareness) was founded in 1993 by Mr John Aini. A native of New Hannover Island, he was working as a Department of Fisheries sea-cucumber surveyor at the time and realized that he needed to do something for his local area. He returned to his home village and founded Ailan Awareness. Since then he has been reaching out to coastal communities around New Hannover and New Ireland on the subject of marine-resource management and the need to make better choices for the future.

John Aini helped create the first management plan and locally managed marine area in his home village of Lovangai in 2007. Following this he succeeded in establishing 14 management plans and helped to write New Ireland's first marine resource-management law, which incorporates all the local management plans. He also established the Solwara (Saltwater) School on the outskirts of Kavieng. The school is a home base for Ailan Awareness, but also runs education programmes for school groups and local adults, and is a place where local communities can come for support in writing their own management plans.

SURFING AT KAVIENG

One of the most interesting resource-management plans in the Kavieng area is not for biological resources, but for surfing. The area faces the expanse of the Pacific Ocean, which brings large swells and warm waters that attract surfers from all over the world. Papua New Guinea is still a relative frontier for surfing, and the budding surfing industry in Kavieng was determined not to make the mistakes often made elsewhere. Many of the world's best-known surfing places quickly became over-crowded and suffered from too many surfers trying to access the same waves. This led to violence and loss of prestige for the areas. Some global surfing hotspots experimented with having exclusive access to the best surf spots, but with bad results.

In Papua New Guinea the customary tenure meant that surfers needed permission to surf on the reefs of a local community, and often had to pay for that permission. So, Shawn Keane, the owner of the Nusa Island Retreat Resort, worked with other surf entrepreneurs in the area and with John Aini, to pioneer the idea of a 'surf-management plan'. The plan sets quotas for each surf sport around Kavieng – currently at 20 surfers per break – and each visiting international surfer pays a fee to the Niu Ailan Surfriders Alliance, which is allocated to the communities who own the reef resources. In exchange, the communities have a responsibility to keep the reefs and beaches clean, and to keep the reef open to the surfers. While the surfers generally do not impact the marine resources with their activity, the concept of the management plan and quota system has reverberated throughout

New Ireland province. Surf-management plans are springing up along the coast, and local communities are working to extend the concept to birdwatching, trekking and bush walking.

DIVING

There are limited options for diving in Papua New Guinea, but they are all outstanding. Madang Lagoon, Kavieng, Tufi and Milne Bay all have well-known diving resorts. A few live-aboards operate either permanently or seasonally. Papua New Guinea's reefs are spectacular and highly biodiverse, and the country also has a wide array of ship and plane wrecks from the Second World War.

Above: Nusa Island, off Kavieng town, is home to a resort for surfers.

Left: Surfing tourists in Kavieng help manage coral reefs and developed a surf-site management plan with local communities.

TRAINING *and* RESEARCH

AMONG the key activities of the National Plan of Action were commitments to reinvigorate the National Fisheries College and National Mariculture Research Centre, both located in Kavieng. The National Fisheries College was renamed the Institute for Sustainable Marine Resources in 2008, but most people still refer to it as the National Fisheries College. It is associated with the nearby National Mariculture Research Facility on Nago Island just off Kavieng.

The college was built in 1977 as a base for a Japanese pole-and-line fishery, but due to unpaid taxes the government took over the facility, with a mandate to train people to work within the fisheries sectors as boat crew, processing facility staff or fisheries observers. Every purse-seine boat in Papua New Guinea must carry an independent observer who has been trained at the college. With the recent Marine Stewardship Council certification, this is a critical function.

The mariculture facility was rebuilt in 2012 and has facilities for dry and wet labs, pond culture and tanks. The biggest research programme involves the culture of sea cucumbers and helping to restore populations, and ending the ban on sea-cucumber fisheries. The facility also hosts researchers who are learning how to culture a rare species of clownfish for the aquarium trade. With the creation of a technique to raise the fish in a hatchery, wild populations can be saved from over-collection.

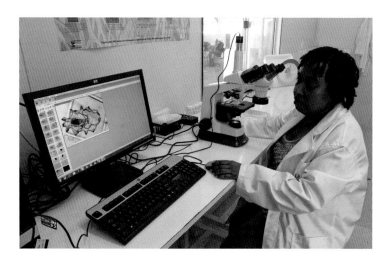

This page: Researchers at the Nago Island Mariculture and Research Facility work with the National Fisheries College to improve production of sea cucumbers and other species.

Opposite: The role of sponges in the ecology of reefs is still relatively unknown, but recent research indicates that they play a much more significant role than was previously thought.

6

THE PHILIPPINES

The Philippines is the northernmost of the six Coral Triangle countries, lying at the apex of the triangle. The archipelago comprises more than 7,000 islands, the South China, Sulu, Sulawesi and Philippine Seas, and the Pacific Ocean. The two largest islands of Luzon and Mindanao, to the north and south respectively, bracket a large group of islands and water bodies centred on the Visayan Sea. An estimated 105 million people live on 300,000 sq km (115,830 sq miles), and the Philippines claims a total marine area (Exclusive Economic Zone) of 2,200,000 sq km (849,425 sq miles). Nearly 50 per cent of the population lives in urban areas, with Manila being by far the biggest city with approximately 11 million people. The next biggest city, Davao, has only 1.5 million people.

Left: Mabini and Tingloy municipalities, better known (incorrectly) as Anilao, are renowned for their colourful reefs and cryptic species.

THE PHILIPPINES

Luzon Strait

BATAN IS.

Itbayat

Batan

PACIFIC
OCEAN

200m
2000m
4000m
6000m
8000m
10000m

● Towns/cities
● National parks

Babuyan

Calayan

Dalupiri

Fuga

BABUYAN IS.

Camiguin

Cape Engaño

Vigan

SIERRA MADRE

LUZON

▲ Mt. Pulog

PHILIPPINE SEA

MANILA

Manila Bay

Anilao

Verde Island Passage

Puerto Galera

Mindoro

Ragay Gulf

Tablas Strait

Sibuyan Sea

Sibuyan

Donsol

Catanduanes

Lagonoy Gulf

Mindoro Strait

CALAMIAN GROUP

Coron

Linapacan Strait

El Nido

Taytay

Cuyo Is.

Dumaran

Apurahuan

Puerto Princesa

Palawan

Cagayancillo Islands

Tubbataha Reefs National Park ●

SULU SEA

Balabac

Balabac Strait

Kudat

Turtle Islands

MALAYSIA

Sabah

PHILIPPINES

Panay

Iloilo

Panay Gulf

Masbate

Visayan Sea

Cadiz

Cebu

Negros

Dumaguete

Siquijor

Calbayog

Samar

Samar Sea

Malapascua Island

Tacloban

Leyte Gulf

Leyte

Bohol

Surigao

Siargao

Bohol Sea

Cagayan de Oro ●

MINDANAO

▲ Mt. Apo

Davao

Davao Gulf

Mindanao Trench

Zamboanga

Moro Gulf

Samales Group

Jolo

SULU ARCHIPELAGO

General Santos

SULAWESI SEA

Sarangani

0   100 Miles

0   100   200 Kilometres

As part of the Pacific Ring of Fire the Philippines has many tectonic faults and volcanoes; it lies within the 'typhoon belt' of the Western Pacific Ocean and is hit regularly by large storms. The Philippine islands are the result of complex tectonic movements, with several plates having come together over geological time. To the east of the country the Philippine Sea – a part of the Pacific Ocean – borders some of the deepest trenches in the world, reaching depths below 10,000 m (32,808 ft). The northernmost islands, north of Luzon,

nearly reach Taiwan and are famous for the presence of migrating Humpback Whales (*Megaptera novaeangliae*) in the spring. The cluster of islands that comprises the Visayan group includes Cebu, Samar and Leyte, faces the Pacific Ocean to the east and bears the initial impact of many typhoons that strike the country (Spalding, Ravilious & Green, 2001).

To the south is the Philippine's second biggest island, Mindanao, with the highest mountain – Mount Apo. The Sulu archipelago stretches to the west of Mindanao towards Malaysian Borneo, and separates the basins of the Sulu Sea from the Sulawesi Sea. In the south-west of the Philippines is the elongated island of Palawan that forms the boundary between the South China Sea to the west and the Sulu Sea. Running through the centre of the deep Sulu Sea the Cagayan Ridge reaches the surface at a few points, and several large atolls and small islands dot the centre of the sea. Most of the larger islands were once covered with tropical rainforests. With so many islands giving the Philippines a long coastline and favourable conditions of warm, clear waters, the Philippines is rich in coral reefs, mangroves and seagrasses.

Extensive areas of coral reef are found throughout the country, although they are noticeably absent in select areas and near river mouths with high freshwater and sediment discharge. Notable reef areas include the double barrier reef north of Bohol in the Visayan Sea, the Tubbataha atoll in the centre of the Sulu Sea and the submerged barrier-reef system west of Palawan. Very little is known about many of the Philippines' reef systems, particularly in the Sulu Archipelago. The total number of species in any taxon is still hotly debated, as is the richest particular area in the Coral Triangle. At least one major study (Carpenter & Springer, 2005) identified the Visayas as the 'centre of the centre' of marine biodiversity. There are an estimated 577 species of coral, 3,053 fish species, 42 mangroves and 16 seagrasses in the Philippines (State of the Coral Triangle Report: Philippines).

Below: The tiny islets of Tubbataha Reefs are home to important colonies of seabirds including terns and boobies.

The PEOPLE

MORE than 55 million people in the Philippines live within 10 km (6 miles) of the coast. More than a quarter of Filipinos live below the official poverty line, and the per capita gross domestic product was US $4,500 in 2013. Despite the high poverty rate, the Philippines has a high literacy rate and a strong national education programme (CIA, 2012). Fisheries are a major source of employment and food security. More than 1.5 million people were directly involved with fisheries in 2011.

Right: Showing off a prized catch of Mahi Mahi (*Coryphaena hippurus*).

Opposite: Small pelagics are landed at the massive processing centre in Navotas outside Manila.

Below: Throughout the Philippines, *bancas* are a primary mode of transport, as well as being used for fishing and SCUBA diving.

THREATS *to* MARINE BIODIVERSITY

IN the Philippines threats to marine biodiversity are widespread and pervasive. Overcrowding on the islands, poor land-use practices, overfishing and extensive use of destructive fishing techniques have devastated Philippine coral reefs. Reef surveys from as early as the late 1970s indicated that human pressure was degrading the reef ecosystems, with only 5 per cent considered to be in excellent condition. By 2004 that figure had dropped to 1 per cent, and most of those were in protected areas (Burke, Reytar, Spalding & Perry, 2012).

The 2012 Reefs at Risk Revisited in the Coral Triangle study modelled threats to coral reefs in the Philippines and painted a grim picture. Except for a few reefs in protected areas, far from land, almost all are impacted by human activity. Two-thirds are estimated to be in the very high or high threat category for local threats of overfishing, destructive fishing, land-based pollution and coastal development. Overfishing threatens 98 per cent of the reefs. Destructive fishing is thought to have been reduced in certain areas, but is still estimated to threaten 70 per cent of reefs.

DESTRUCTIVE FISHING

The practice of muro-ami, where lines of divers and swimmers pound a reef with rocks attached to the end of a stick or line, has mostly been eliminated. As the corals were broken and crushed under the weight of the rocks, fish were scared away from the reef and the swimmers drove them into a waiting net. Once one of the Philippines' top fish-production methods, this system was responsible for destroying vast areas of reef.

Now the destructive fishing methods are mostly limited to the illegal practices of dynamite fishing and cyanide fishing. Blast fishing started with the use of remaining Second World War ordinance, but now 'bombs' are home-made with fertilizers and a bottle. The explosion kills or stuns fish within a radius of 10 m (33 ft) and can destroy a small patch of coral. The bombs are cheap to make and easy to deploy, resulting in some areas being compared with 'carpet-bombing' sites. Cyanide is used by divers to stun target fish for the aquarium trade and live food-fish trade.

SEDIMENTATION AND POLLUTION

With such a high coastal population and poor land-use practices, including large-scale forestry and illegal mining, more than half of the reefs are impacted by sedimentation or pollution from human settlements. Seagrasses and mangroves have not fared much better. Only 247,000 ha (610,350 acres) of an estimated original 400,000 (988,422 acres) of mangroves remain, and 30 to 50 per cent of seagrasses have been lost (Coral Triangle Initiative, 2012).

MUNICIPAL AND COMMERCIAL FISHING

Fisheries are an important component of the Philippine economy. The two main categories of fisheries are municipal and commercial fisheries. Municipal fisheries are relatively small in scale and operate within 15 km (9 miles) of the coast. They are governed and managed by respective local government, with municipal mayors and councils having direct authority. Commercial fisheries are those operating with bigger boats more than 15 km (9 miles) from the coast. The majority of municipal fishing boats are traditional *bancas* with long, narrow main hulls and twin outriggers providing stability.

Wild-caught fish are critically important for Philippine food security, but only make up about half of the total production. Aquaculture produces some fish for local consumption, but most aquaculture production is seaweed to derive carrageenan as a stabilizing agent in industrial food production. In 2010 municipal fisheries produced slightly more than the commercial fisheries at 1.37 million tons and 1.25 million tons respectively. Small pelagic fish such as sardines, anchovies and mackerel are some of the most commonly consumed fish in the Philippines, but stocks have been declining since the 1980s. Tuna are a major fishery, accounting for 12 per cent of national fish landings, but most are for export markets. The live reef-fish trade targets speciality fish for consumption and aquaria. Many of the fish for the specialized trade caught with the sodium cyanide solution are either ornamental reef fish or high-level predators including groupers and Humphead Wrasse (Bureau of Fisheries and Aquatic Resources, 2011).

DIVING

THE Philippines is a marine-tourism and SCUBA-diving paradise. Nearly every province has at least one dive shop or diving-oriented resort. Some scientists consider the Philippines to be the centre of coral-reef fish biodiversity richness, and a variety of unusual and cryptic fish species can be found at many dive sites. Despite the high human population density on most islands, the continued use of destructive fishing practices and general overfishing, there are many excellent dive sites throughout the islands. Many of the best are protected areas because the Philippines has established hundreds of marine protected areas along its coasts.

Tubbataha Reefs National Park is the crown jewel of Philippine diving. The reefs are far from the closest local community and can only be visited via live-aboard boats during the short window of fair weather between March and June each year. Divers lucky enough to visit are treated to clear waters, huge walls of coral, and the possibility of seeing manta rays, tuna and Tiger Sharks (*Galeocerdo cuvier*).

Closer to Manila two areas bordering the Verde Island Passage are popular with divers from the Philippines and around the world. Anilao, on the island of Luzon, is north of the Passage, while south of the Passage is the dive resort concentration of Puerto Galera, Mindoro Island. Both spots have many resorts catering to the needs of divers, and are renowned for their fish richness and the presence of numerous small, cryptic and highly sought-after animals like ghost pipefish (*Solenostomus* spp.), frogfish (Antennariidae) and Pfeffer's Flamboyant Cuttlefish (*Metasepia pfefferi*).

Left: The Six-barred Angelfish (*Pomacanthus sexistriatus*) is one of several large angelfish to be found on Coral Triangle reefs.

Below: Sombrero Island between Tingloy and Mabini is one of the most famous dive sites in Anilao, known for big schools of colourful fish and soft corals.

Opposite: The gill rakers of manta rays (here *Manta birostris*) are increasingly valued in the Chinese traditional medicine markets, threatening the future of these ocean giants.

At the northern tip of Cebu, Malapascua Island is famous for the unusual presence of Pelagic Thresher Sharks (*Alopias pelagicus*) that come to a particular seamount for cleaning every morning. The sharks come to the top of the seamount that rises from several hundreds of metres deep to a depth of 20 m (66 ft) to be cleaned by wrasses and other fish that specialize in removing parasites and dead tissue from the sharks. Thresher Sharks are deep-water species that hunt in the dark waters below the photic zone. They come to the relatively shallow Monad Shoal early in the morning before the sun is high, so divers venture out at 5 a.m. to see them.

Two of the most famous diving locations in the Philippines are the incomparable El Nido and Coron areas. The municipalities at the northern end of Palawan Island are famous for weathered limestone outcrops that help produce crystal-clear water, white-sand beaches, dramatic topside landscapes, rich coral reefs and incomparable wreck diving

This page: Several species of crab, shrimp and fish make their home in the anus of sea cucumbers.

Opposite above: At Monad Shoal near Malapascua Island, Pelagic Thresher Sharks come near to the surface early in the morning to be cleaned by small fish.

Opposite below: The Short Pouch Pygmy Pipehorse (*Acentronura breviperula*) has a prehensile tail that it uses to hold on to seagrasses. It grows to a maximum of 5 cm (2 in) long.

NATIONAL PLAN *of* ACTION

THE CTI National Plan of Action for the Philippines was drafted in 2009. It is closely aligned to the Regional Plan of Action (see page 33) and will be implemented for at least ten years. The plan is led jointly by the Department of Environment and Natural Resources and the Department of Agriculture's Bureau, but with input from many government agencies, several large NGOs and academia. The plan has a vision statement that focuses on biodiversity and ecological integrity, while sustaining the needs of people in a collaborative fashion.

The national plan revolves around the concept of integrated coastal management and five specific goals relating to those of the regional plan. The integrated coastal management is codified in Philippine law and attempts to overcome the difficulties encountered when several different user groups and management agencies are managing the same area, but not in coordination with each other. Often the management practices are in conflict with each other: for example, the transport and shipping management may want to develop better harbour facilities in a place that the environment managers have identified as an important habitat for conservation or fisheries. Integrated coastal management is expected to help break the sectoral barriers that have been set between government agencies, and between the government and the private sector and other components of civil society. The goals of the national plan are detailed below.

Under Goal 1 the plan has two targets: to designate priority seascapes, and to ensure that the priority seascapes are effectively managed. The Philippines has already designated the Sulu-Sulawesi Marine Ecoregion as a priority seascape. Actions to achieve the targets include replicating the Sulu-Sulawesi process for the South China Sea, the Northeast Philippine Pacific Seaboard and the Southeast Philippine Pacific Seaboard.

Under Goal 2 the ecosystem approach to the management of fisheries and other marine resources must be fully applied. The ecosystem approach to management of fisheries is not well defined, but usually entails a shift from single-species management of fisheries to include the health of ecosystems and fish stocks, impact on societal needs, and taking into account the opinions and input of resources in management. This goal has four targets in the plan, relating to having a strong policy framework in place, improving incomes and livelihoods for coastal communities, and ensuring that tuna and live reef fisheries are sustainable.

Goal 3 proposes that marine protected areas be established and effectively managed, including community-based resource utilization and management. The target is to contribute to a Coral Triangle-wide system of marine protected areas, and to eventually have 20 per cent of each habitat type in strict protected areas. Specific actions include:

- Implementing the existing national marine sanctuary strategy and the Sulu-Sulawesi Marine Ecoregion marine protected area strategy.
- Identifying other 'marine key biodiversity areas' with a protected area in each.
- Building capacity for local governments to manage protected areas.
- Developing strategies for rehabilitating and managing mangroves and seagrasses.

Goal 4 aspires to achieve climate-change adaptation measures. One target of the plan is to implement early actions for climate-change adaptation, including conducting vulnerability assessments for extreme weather, identifying potential adaptation measures and building infrastructure with climate-change adaptations as part of the design. The second target focuses on building a network of centres of excellence on climate-change adaptation.

Goal 5 aims to improve the status of threatened animals and plants, including sharks, sea turtles, seabirds, marine mammals, corals, seagrasses, mangroves and others that are threatened as they are identified. This includes, among other actions, conducting assessments of threatened species populations particularly for marine endemic bony fish, wrasses and blennies, and coral-reef fish; and implementing individual national plans of action for sharks, turtles and Dugongs.

The national plan is to be overseen by a CTI Coordination Committee with representation from the Department of Foreign Affairs, Department of Finance, National Economic Development Authority, two NGO representatives, two academic institution representatives and one representative from the business sector. The plan includes chapters for securing financial resources for the implementation of several guiding principles, and a monitoring strategy for the entire plan (Republic of the Philippines, 2009).

Opposite: The karst formations of El Nido and Coron make for spectacular land and seascapes.

COASTAL *and* MARINE CONSERVATION

THE Philippines has a long history of coastal and marine conservation. The Department of Natural Resources and Environment and the Bureau of Fisheries and Aquatic Resources are the two main national agencies responsible for planning and monitoring marine resources in the Philippines. In 1991 the management of coastal waters was decentralized and placed under the purview of the municipal governments. The national fisheries law mandates that each municipality declare 15 per cent of its waters as fish sanctuaries. As a result, the Philippines has the most marine protected areas (more than 1,600) in the Coral Triangle.

The sheer number of protected areas in the Philippines is a testament to the success of the government, NGOs and academia in spreading the word about the benefits of marine conservation. The majority of the protected areas are small and collaboratively managed by local community groups and the local government. Some are well managed and helping to restore fisheries and the environment. There is, however, a lack of information about most of them, and a large proportion of them are considered 'paper parks' without any management on the ground. The government agencies responsible for managing the areas are generally understaffed and underfunded, and therefore have difficulty in effectively managing the areas. Even the location and boundaries of almost half the parks are unknown.

Under the Philippine Marine Sanctuary Strategy there is a target to have 10 per cent of the seas in protected areas by 2020, with representation in each of the six identified biogeographical areas (South China Sea, Visayas, Northern Philippine Sea, Southern Philippine Sea, Sulawesi Sea and Sulu Sea). More than 80 per cent of the protected areas are relatively small at less than 100 ha (247 acres). Some larger ones have been declared through the National Integrated Protected Areas System.

TUBBATAHA REEFS NATIONAL PARK

The largest marine protected area in the Philippines, at 970 sq km (375 sq miles), is the Tubbataha Reefs National Park. The park protects three remote reefs in the middle of the Sulu Sea. The core of the protected area is made up of two reef atolls that emerge from the Cagayan Ridge bisecting the Sulu Sea from north to south. The atolls were formed millennia ago when volcanic islands emerged from the deep and reefs fringed their shores. As the volcanoes eroded away, they left the reefs in their wake. Now the two reefs measure around 16 km (10 miles) and 4.5 km (3 miles) long respectively, and about 4 km (2½ miles) wide each, with some scattered islets in the lagoons.

In 2006 the park was expanded by 200 per cent to include the submerged Jessie Beazely Reef to the north-west of the north atoll. Other than having a permanent ranger station, the reefs are completely devoid of human habitation, and home only to colonies of seabirds and the rich marine life found beneath the waves. Tubbataha is subject to several monsoons and can experience rough seas and large waves. A calm season between March and June once allowed limited fishing; today, SCUBA divers have the privilege of exploring during the three-month dive season.

Surveys have shown that Tubbataha is one of the most biodiverse reef areas in the Philippines, with more than 600 fish species and 360 coral species. The reefs are also important places for marine mammals, commercially important pelagic fish and two marine turtle species. Perhaps most importantly, it has been suggested that Tubbataha is a strategic source of fish larvae supplying large parts of the Sulu Sea with fish. Currents that sweep around the Tubbataha Reefs pick up the fertilized eggs and larvae that are generated there and carry them to populated areas of Palawan, Mindoro and the Visayas (Dygico, 2006).

The reefs were traditional fishing and collecting grounds for generations of sea nomads and other communities from the southern Philippines, as well as residents of the nearby Cagayancillo islands. Due to the remoteness of the place and the rough seas only short trips in small, sail-powered vessels could be made, so the visitors would fill their boats with fish, turtles and birds' eggs for every trip. The distance and challenges of the journey probably resulted in minimal impact on the resources from these brief forays.

In the mid-1980s sails were replaced with engines, and fishermen from further north in the Visayas also discovered the riches of Tubbataha. The Visayan fishermen introduced blast fishing and cyanide fishing, and taught them to their counterparts from Cagayancillo. Through the use of such destructive techniques, fishermen were able to increase their catches considerably in a short time, making the long trips worthwhile. Eventually, some of the Visayan fishermen even settled in Cagayancillo and intermarried with locals. It did not take long for the modern techniques to destroy what had been sustained for so long, and the Tubbataha Reefs began to suffer. Around the same time, recreational SCUBA divers discovered Tubbataha and began making regular visits. They would sometimes camp on the islands or go fishing while on dive trips, and they became alarmed by the destruction.

In 1988 the Tubbataha Reef National Marine Park, as it was then known, was officially declared by presidential proclamation, and it was granted World Heritage Status by UNESCO in 1993.

However, it was not until 1999 that the current management system was finally established. For the first decade of the park's existence several management systems were attempted but failed for various reasons, including having the management bodies situated too far from the reefs themselves. In 1999 a third iteration of a management board was approved by the Palawan government, and this one was to prove more resilient than its predecessors. The management board established the Tubbataha Management Office to run the park in 2001. Now the office, based in Puerto Princesa, reports to both the provincial and national governments, and is responsible for implementing the management plan approved by the board.

The original park-management plan was updated in 2011. It is focused on overcoming the challenges posed by the remoteness of the reefs, the illegal fishermen that come from around the Philippines and East Asia, the solid waste and litter that washes up on the beaches, the potential for oil and gas development in the Sulu Sea near the park, increased shipping traffic and building a constituency for the park with stakeholders. Most management actions centre around enforcement of the rules and regulations, and awareness raising among stakeholders.

With no fishing or any other extractive activity of any sort allowed in the park, keeping an eye on anyone who might try to illegally enter it is the primary management activity. Enforcement of the park rules and regulations is conducted by a small team with members from the Philippine Navy, Coastguard, Tubbataha Management Office and local Cagayancillo municipal government. The team is on duty year round, and individuals undertake three-month rotations of duty on the remote outpost. Before each rotation the contingent is given training on the specific protocols of the park management, the ecology of Tubbataha reefs, equipment maintenance and law-enforcement procedures.

At the beginning of the enforcement programmes the park used law enforcement and prosecution of illegal fishermen extensively. This lasted for about three years and the message was clear to local communities, resulting in the decline of intrusions. One of the real keys to the management and success of Tubbataha is the engagement of the local communities of Cagayancillo. As their awareness of marine-conservation issues grew, they even created

Above: Monitoring of the marine environment at Tubbataha is done in collaboration with NGOs and universities from around the Philppines.

their own protected areas within their municipal waters and have seen their immediate environment improve. With more resources on their home reefs, there is less need to make the long voyage to Tubbataha. As part of the incentive for the communities of Cagayancillo, 10 per cent of Tubbataha entry fees are invested in a fund for infrastructure and schools in the municipality (Tubbataha Protected Area Management Board, 2011).

The park continues to deal with several major issues. The occasional incursion by foreign fishermen can have big impacts on the resources. In recent years boats from China and Vietnam have been apprehended in Tubbataha waters with cargoes of endangered sea turtles and Napoleon Wrasse (*Cheilinus undulatus*).

A different, and unexpected, kind of incursion has manifested itself recently with several high-profile ships being grounded on the reefs. In 2005 Greenpeace's ship *Rainbow Warrior*, ironically, ran aground on Tubbataha and destroyed nearly 100 sq m (1,076 sq ft) of the reef. In January 2013 a US Navy ship, USS *Guardian*, was grounded on the reef. The US Navy claimed in some reports that its maps did not match the location of the reef, but the fact that the ship grounded very near the lighthouse raised suspicions. A third

grounding on the reef occurred in April 2013, when a Chinese fishing vessel hit the reef. These groundings can all be charged with illegal entry into the park without a permit and fined for the damage to the reef. Another alarming development has been the exploration for oil and gas in the Sulu Sea near the park boundaries.

With a comprehensive programme of park management, including enforcement and tourism, conducting information and awareness programmes about the importance of the park with local communities and donors, managing research within the park and helping the communities of Cagayancillo to manage their marine resources, the Tubbataha Management Office is stretched thin. The park is managed like an independent organization, although it is part of the Philippine government and receives no federal government funding allocation. Just over half of the budget in recent years has come from entry-permit revenues, with the remaining portion coming from grants and the Palawan provincial government.

The park has been an undoubted success. Monitoring of fish and corals inside it shows not only healthy resources, but also good recovery progress from incidents of coral bleaching and Crown-of-thorns Starfish outbreaks. Monitoring surveys have shown increasing

Left: Whale Shark tourism in Donsol is strictly regulated. In Oslob there are few regulations and visitors frequently dive with the giant fish.

Opposite: The Napoleon Wrasse is so prized as a live food fish that the trade has depleted populations. Trade in the fish is now banned in many areas of the Coral Triangle.

coral cover since a bleaching event in 2008, and divers regularly report sightings of animals that are largely absent on many other Philippine reefs, including Tiger Sharks, manta rays and Napoleon Wrasse.

DONSOL AND WHALE SHARKS

Donsol is a small municipality at the very southern tip of Luzon Island. Until the mid-1990s it was just an obscure part of Sorsogon Province in the Bicol Region. When some divers ventured into the region they discovered a secret that had been known to the locals for over 100 years – Donsol is a feeding ground for *Butanding*, Whale Sharks. They migrate to the bay off Donsol every March and April to feed in the plankton-rich waters for several months before continuing their annual migration (Pine, 2007).

Whale Sharks are the biggest fish in the world and can reach 20 m (66 ft) in length and more than 34 tons, although most are in the 10–15-m (33–49-ft) range. They are found throughout the world's tropical oceans, are thought to make long annual migrations to various feeding grounds, and return to the same feeding grounds year after year. Despite being the biggest shark in the world, the Whale Shark is not a top predator but feeds much lower on the trophic ladder, filtering plankton from the seas, and it is also known to feed on small shrimps, squid and fish.

While the Whale Shark is not dangerous to humans, humans are dangerous to it. Whale Sharks have been hunted for their meat, fins and skin to the point of being globally Vulnerable on the IUCN Red List, and the international trade is now governed through the Convention on International Trade in Endangered Species (CITES). In the Philippines local communities hunted Whale Sharks for decades on a small scale. In the late 1980s and '90s the hunting increased to the point where Whale Shark sightings became rare around the Philippine islands, except in Donsol, where the sharks were not hunted. It was around the same time that a local SCUBA diver heard stories about the Whale Sharks in Donsol and went to investigate. He found the largest concentration of Whale Sharks in the world.

News of the discovery spread quickly. International scientists and WWF were notified. It is thought that the sharks come to feed on the rich plankton of Donsol's bay. Tourists from around the country and the world started arriving in Donsol to see these amazing fish. The news also attracted hunters from Manila and the Bohol Sea. The local government in Donsol acted fast and declared the bay off their municipality as the Philippine's first Whale Shark Sanctuary, but that did not stop the hunters. Information about Whale Shark kills near Donsol spread through news reports. As a result, Whale Sharks were declared a protected species in March 1998.

The sudden influx of tourists in 1998 overwhelmed the town. The economic opportunity was clear, but the tiny fishing village had no knowledge of tourism or how to regulate interactions with the sharks. Reports of up to 20 boats crowding a single animal, boat collisions and a snorkeller run over by a boat proved that the community needed training and a plan. The municipal council, the newly formed Donsol Municipal Tourism Council and

WWF-Philippines mobilized resources and established a visitor management system and Whale Shark interaction protocols. Local guides received training and a nationwide education programme commenced. The local guides became accredited *Butanding* Interaction Officers, and a system of registration and profit sharing was designed. Tourists had to pay fees and register at a central tourism office before they could board a boat with at least one officer for a tour of the bay. Rules stipulated that tourists could only snorkel, not SCUBA dive, with the sharks, and there could only be six swimmers in the water with one shark at a time.

Today an officer acts as a spotter and rule enforcer as the typical Philippine *banca* with two bamboo outriggers cruises in a search pattern in the bay. When the officer spots a shark in the distance he directs the captain to a spot where the boat will intersect the shark's path, and directs his passengers to prepare to swim. When the boat reaches the spot he instructs the snorkellers into the murky green water. The maximum six swimmers enter the water and wait. Usually within a minute the behemoth appears in the plankton-green water just under the swimmers, gliding quickly through the water. Swimmers are instructed to stay several metres from the fish and not to touch it, although some do not comply with the instructions. In some cases the shark swims past as quickly as it arrived and the divers climb back on board the boat to find the next interaction. Sometimes the shark slows down and the visitors can spend several minutes basking in its presence.

Eventually the municipality limited the tourism interactions to 25 boats per day with a three-hour limit per boat. During the high season a single boat could have several encounters during its allotted time. As demand continued to soar the limit was increased to 60 boats for two hours each. The growing tourism business in Donsol helped to offset some of the losses from declines in small-scale fishing incomes. The plankton-rich waters that attract the Whale Sharks also support a commercial fishery for small pelagics. To help maintain the productivity of the region the municipality established several small marine protected areas along the coast in 2007.

A dramatic decline in Whale Shark numbers was observed from 2010 to 2012, with a resulting drop in tourism numbers. Impacts of climate change or inland pollution have been proposed as proximate causes of a loss of plankton that would limit the numbers of sharks which could feed in the waters off Donsol. The mystery was heightened when it was observed in late 2012 that the sharks were returning to Donsol in November rather than the usual April.

ANILAO: MANAGING DIVING AND FISHING

One of the most popular diving destinations in the Philippines happens to be just over 100 km (62 miles) from Metro Manila and just around the corner from the industrial port city of Batangas. It is part of the Verde Island Passage, an area considered by some scientists to be the centre of global fish diversity (Carpenter & Springer, 2005). Anilao is the popular name for a diving destination that comprises Mabini and Tingloy municipalities in Batangas province. Mabini sits on a peninsula that separates Balayan and Batangas Bays, and forms the northern shores of the Verde Island Passage.

In the 1970s divers from Manila discovered the riches of the seas around the Mabini Peninsula and Tingloy Island. The area came to be known, mistakenly, as Anilao, because that was the name of the town where the divers would park their cars before heading off to dive and camp further down the peninsula. The close proximity to Manila and the variety of fish and corals made it a popular weekend destination, and a number of resorts catering to divers quickly popped up (Salao, Honasan & Sandalo, 2007).

Around the same time the practices of spearfishing with SCUBA, cyanide fishing for aquarium fish and blast fishing were gaining popularity among some groups of fishermen around Balayan Bay. The two quickly came into conflict, and the divers and resorts started campaigns to protect the reefs of Mabini and Tingloy. Starting in the mid-1980s through the mid-1990s, resort owners and the Philippine NGO, Haribon Foundation, worked together to establish several marine protected areas and sanctuaries at some of the most popular dive sites, and passed local laws preventing fishing at those sites.

The destructive fishing took a toll on fish populations at the same time that diving boomed. Many fishermen moved from fishing to working as dive guides or renting their boats to take divers. From the initial attempts to manage diving and conserve the environment, several initiatives started and ended with limited success. Challenges included differences in political agendas between Mabini and Tingloy municipalities. Mabini, on the mainland of Luzon, was the site of most of the dive resorts, while the island of Tingloy had most of the dive sites but with limited infrastructure and few resorts. Early attempts to establish sanctuaries and enforce them with voluntary wardens called *Bantay Dagat* (Sea Guardians) were challenged by a lack of funding and resources. It was not until the early 2000s that Mabini and Tingloy established a coordinated system of charging a diving access fee shared between the two municipalities. Now, each municipality has a contingent of *Bantay Dagat* to patrol the seas, watch for commercial fishing boats trying to illegally encroach into coastal waters, monitor diving activities and check that all divers pay their daily diving fees.

Opposite: Anthias, cup corals and featherstars make for a colourful scene typical of Anilao.

TAYTAY AND GROUPERS

Groupers are considered a delicacy in southern Chinese cuisine. They are prized for their white, flaky flesh and delicate taste. Some species, like the Red Coral Grouper (*Plectropomus leopardus*) and similar red groupers, are further prized for their bright red colour – a sign of good luck and prosperity. Many Chinese seafood restaurants keep live fish in tanks until it is ordered. In Beijing, prices can reach US $220 per kilogram. The island province of Palawan is one of the trade centres in Southeast Asia, and one municipality, Taytay, is striving to make it sustainable.

Groupers are a top predator on reefs. They can live to be 14 years old, reproduce only after reaching 2–3 years of age, and come together in large aggregations to spawn. This makes them vulnerable to overfishing, and a population of breeding adults can be easily wiped off a reef. Removing top predators upsets the ecological balance on a reef, weakening the resiliency of the ecosystem.

Overfishing is just one of the problems with the live grouper trade. Due to the groupers' high value – a poor fisherman can double his weekly income with one adult grouper – fishermen will go to great lengths to find them. As adult groupers become rare, fishermen resort to other methods. They search for elusive fish with an air compressor and hookah, subjecting themselves to the bends during long, deep dives. They often squirt the fish with a solution of sodium cyanide to stun it, making it easy to grab. If the fish retreats to the safety of the corals, cyanide is squirted into the crevices and the rocks are broken to extract the stunned fish. The exposed corals may eventually die and the broken rocks kill decades of coral growth. Adult fish caught this way have a higher possibility of death, hence there is a greater urgency to sell them immediately. The juvenile fish, too small for a meal, are kept in sea cages and fed until they are an ideal size for sale. Often they are fed with 'trash fish' or fish caught with explosives – another fishing method that devastates coral reefs.

Attempts have been made to regulate and improve this trade since the late 1990s. It is now so big that it is a major focus of WWF and a focal issue for an international treaty to conserve the Coral Triangle. So far, all attempts have failed and the trade is still unsustainable. The Philippines remains a major source of Red Coral Grouper despite having taken the major step of banning the export of all live food fish in 1998 unless it was cultured.

Palawan is renowned for its exceptional biodiversity and natural environment. It enjoys a special administrative status, has its own laws, and wild fish are still exportable from some areas of the island but banned in others. The municipality of Coron, at the northern end of Palawan, was an early centre of the trade, but when grouper populations crashed in the early 2000s, the trade moved to other areas. The municipality of Taytay lies 170 km (106 miles) north of the capital city of Puerto Princesa. Taytay is the current centre of the live reef-fish trade, with more than 1,000 fishermen in the area operating an estimated 2,000 fish cages.

Right: Coral Hind (*Cephalopholis miniata*) are sometimes confused with other red groupers that are highly prized in the live reef-fish trade.

Opposite: In Tatay groupers and wrasses are kept at depth until they grow into marketable size. Keeping them at depth is thought to maintain their desirable red colour.

WWF is making a huge push in Palawan to support the government's efforts to achieve sustainability. The municipality of Taytay is one of the best examples of management in the entire Coral Triangle. All fishermen, cage keepers and traders must be licensed, and several areas where the fish gather to reproduce are protected. The use of protected areas is mandated in the Philippines fisheries law, but the minimum amount of 15 per cent of municipal waters may not be enough for the groupers. The cages are all built to hold juvenile fish, and taking juvenile fish off the reef means that there are no adults to reproduce. Despite its good efforts, Taytay is still being overfished (Salao et al., 2007).

The trade is important enough that it was high on the agenda of Governor Jose Alvarez when he was elected in 2013. Just north of Taytay, the mayor of El Nido banned the trade in order to protect reefs and attract more tourists. While banning the trade is one of the governor's options, WWF and the mayor of Taytay, Mr Romy Salvame, are against it. There are concerns that the government lacks the capacity to enforce a ban, potentially forcing the trade underground. The mayor sees that the trade has brought prosperity to his municipality. He says that it allows his constituents to buy metal roofs for their houses and send their children to university.

The holy grail of a sustainable live reef-fish trade is full-cycle aquaculture, where young fish are bred in captivity and raised completely in tanks. For some species this is already a reality, but for the highly prized Red Coral Groupers there is a sticking point in getting them to live beyond the first three or four weeks. Palawan Aquaculture Corporation in Coron says that it overcame the obstacles in 2013 and plans to start marketing the fish in 2014. The company's head aquaculturist, Ms Elsie Tech, says that the owner of Palawan Aquaculture is hoping that other people will start farming Red Coral Groupers soon, too. The Chinese market is so massive that it can easily absorb other players. Right now the company is attempting to produce the fish in the deep red colour preferred in Chinese restaurants. Cultured fish are paler than wild ones, so the company is experimenting with dyes and other techniques to make them look more appealing for the restaurant clientele.

Unfortunately, WWF's experience of getting live reef-fish traders to voluntarily adopt better practices has not gone well. Consumers in China and Hong Kong are not yet ready to pay a premium for sustainable seafood, and traders in the Coral Triangle will not change their practices until the market demands and pays for it. The recent Chinese government ban on extravagant dinner bills from government officials may also benefit groupers, but this remains to be seen. It is an encouraging sign that there is awareness of the issue and sustainability might be on the horizon. However, until groupers are cultured on a large scale they will continue to come from the wild, and contribute to overfishing and destructive fishing.

7

SOLOMON ISLANDS

The Solomon Islands is the easternmost country of the Coral Triangle. The archipelago stretches nearly 1,500 km (930 miles) from Papua New Guinea in the west to Vanuatu further east. The South Pacific Ocean lies to the north and the Solomon Sea and the Coral Sea buffet the southern islands. The small land area of 28,000 sq km (10,810 sq miles) belies the Solomon Islands' position as one of the world's biggest archipelagos with nearly 1.6 million sq km (617,763 sq miles) of claimed sea territory.

Left: Anthias and other fish school around a colony of fire corals (*Millepora* spp.). Fire corals look like corals but are actually a colonial hydrozoa.

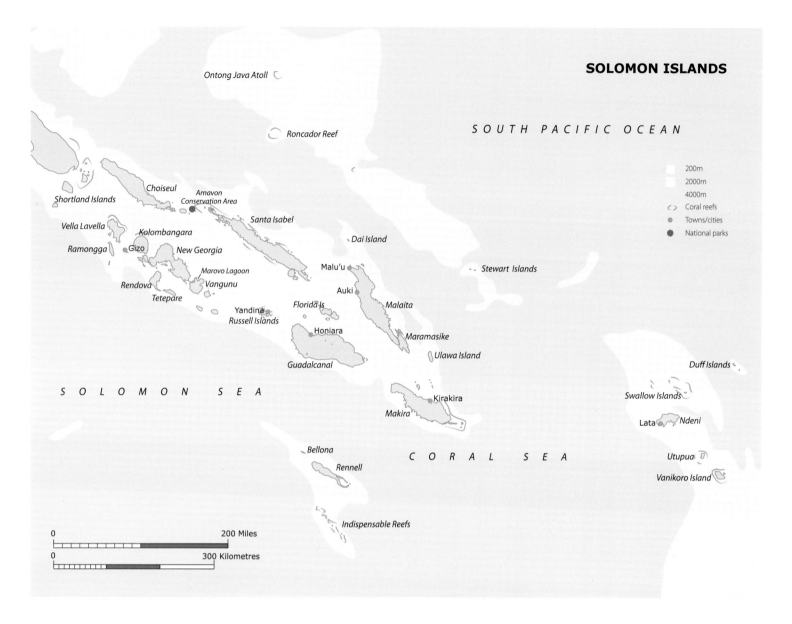

SOLOMON ISLANDS

SOUTH PACIFIC OCEAN

Ontong Java Atoll

Roncador Reef

	200m
	2000m
	4000m
⌒⊃	Coral reefs
●	Towns/cities
●	National parks

Shortland Islands
Choiseul
Arnavon Conservation Area
Santa Isabel
Vella Lavella
Kolombangara
Dai Island
Ramongga
Gizo
New Georgia
Marovo Lagoon
Malu'u
Stewart Islands
Rendova
Vangunu
Auki
Tetepare
Yandina Russell Islands
Florida Is
Malaita
Honiara
Maramasike
Guadalcanal
Ulawa Island
Duff Islands
Swallow Islands
Kirakira
Lata Ndeni
Makira
Utupua
Bellona
Vanikoro Island
Rennell

SOLOMON SEA

CORAL SEA

Indispensable Reefs

0   200 Miles
0   300 Kilometres

The Solomon Islands were formed through complex tectonic activity as the Pacific Plate dove under the Australian Plate. The continued tectonic activity results in the Solomon Islands experiencing frequent earthquakes and volcanic eruptions. Seven large islands, ranging from 140 to 200 km (87–124 miles) long but rarely more than 50 km (31 miles) wide, form two parallel island arcs in the centre of the country. There are just under 1,000 islands, many of them medium sized and tiny coral cays. Guadalcanal is the largest island and the location of the national capital, Honiara. Malaita Island has the biggest population with nearly one-sixth of the entire country living there.

Several far-flung island groups extend the country's borders far from the main island groups. The Santa Cruz group, forming the province of Temotu, borders Vanuatu and is more than 300 km (186 miles) east of the main island arcs. An enormous atoll, Ontong Java, sits north of Choiseul Island, and has a small resident population. To the south of the main group, Bellona, Rennell and

the Indispensable Reefs lie between the Solomon and Coral Seas (Spalding, Ravilious & Green, 2001).

The large islands are mountainous and many of the small islands are the remnants of volcanoes. There are two active volcanoes in the Solomon Islands and several dormant ones. South of New Georgia Island is Kavachi, an active submarine volcano that occasionally emerges from the sea before quickly eroding away. The southernmost island, Rennell, is the world's largest uplifted coral atoll and is listed as a UNESCO World Heritage Site. New Georgia's Marovo Lagoon, considered to be the biggest marine lagoon in the world, displays an excellent example of a double barrier reef at its southern end, and has been proposed as a World Heritage Site. Most of the islands have fringing reefs with numerous small lagoons interspersed with patch reefs among them. On Choiseul and Santa Isabel islands there are ecologically interesting fjord formations. Tetepare Island is the largest island in the South Pacific without a permanent human settlement. There is one ecolodge on the island, but no communities.

Left: The Solomon Islands are dotted with tiny islets surrounded by healthy coral reefs.

Below: A 2004 survey by TNC found 494 coral species in the Solomon Islands.

The PEOPLE

THE Solomon Islands experienced one of the world's highest population growth rates in the early 2000s. While the growth has slowed considerably, the population is still expected to reach nearly 600,000 by 2015. More than 100,000 people occupy the most populous island, Malaita. Most Solomon Islanders are of Melanesian origin, with several small Polynesian groups on remote islands and several communities of people who were relocated from the Gilbert Islands (now Kiribati) in the 1960s. More than 80 per cent of Solomon Islanders live in rural areas and depend on gardens and natural resources for their daily livelihoods. The civil unrest that gripped the country from 1999 to 2003 saw many people moving back to their native provinces and islands, and returning to a reliance on the bounty of the land and sea to survive. With a per capita gross domestic product of US $3,400 in 2012 and a literacy rate of 84 per cent, the Solomon Islands face extreme challenges in developing and managing their natural resources in a sustainable manner. More than 85 per cent of the Solomon Islands' land, coral reefs and near-shore fishing grounds fall within a system of traditional ownership by tribal or community groups, making management by the central government nearly impossible.

Above: More than 80 per cent of Solomon Islands families rely on fishing for their daily nutrition.

Below: Shells, crabs and fish fill the market in Honiara.

ECONOMIC VALUES *of the* SEA

VERY little is known about the coral reefs, mangroves and seagrass resources of the Solomon Islands. A major expedition led by TNC in 2004 surveyed the main island groups and placed the Solomon Islands firmly in the ecological boundaries of the Coral Triangle, with a total of 494 coral species and 1,019 coral-reef fish species identified. Njari Island in Gizo recorded the highest single-dive fish species count outside of Indonesia's Raja Ampat Islands. The expedition identified extensive seagrass beds throughout the area surveyed and found ten species of seagrass, with the largest concentrations being around Malaita Island (Green et al., 2006).

FISHING

The largest commercial fishery in the Solomon Islands is for tuna. As one of the biggest archipelagic states in the Pacific Ocean, the Solomon Islands has extraordinary access to one of the richest tuna fisheries in the world. Solomon Islands is a member of the regional Parties of the Nauru Agreement accord that links eight Pacific nations to manage tuna stocks jointly. The countries control the number of days that can be fished for tuna in their collective national waters, and can exchange fishing days between them.

Most of the tuna are caught with pole and lines, long-lines or purse-seines. In long-line fisheries a single boat can deploy one fishing line that can stretch for 20–30 km (12–19 miles) and dangle up to 2,500 hooks. Purse-seines use large nets that encircle a school of fish and close the net from the bottom. There are several national fishing companies in the Solomon Islands, but distant water fishing fleets from the USA, Taiwan, Korea and Japan also fish extensively in the country's waters. The fees for a day of fishing can range from US $5,000 to $8,000, thus generating significant income for the government of the Solomon Islands. With part of the funds it uses several monitoring vessels and on-board observers to keep track of the fishing operations and strive to reduce illegal incursions and practices.

DIVING

The Solomon Islands have numerous opportunities for SCUBA diving. The infrastructure for tourism is still developing and many areas are not yet equipped for tourism, but offer pristine beaches and snorkelling. Diving resorts can be found in several areas, especially in Western Province or via one of two live-aboard boats operating out of Honiara. In late 2013 the airstrip in the capital of Western Province, Gizo, was sealed, making it the third all-weather airport

Left: The Solomon Islands have agreements with several distant water fleets to fish tuna in the country's waters.

on the islands. Marovo Lagoon, Gizo and Tetepare are some of the best-known diving destinations.

Besides the vast number of healthy reefs and abundant fish, the Solomon Islands also offer interesting Second World War wreck diving. Some of the fiercest battles of the Pacific campaign were fought around these islands, with the Battle of Guadalcanal being the best known. So many ships were sunk off the capital, Honiara, that the strait between Guadalcanal and Florida Islands is now called Iron Bottom Sound. Around Gizo and Munda there are several easily accessed Japanese and Allied war planes, as well as a Japanese supply ship, the *Toa Maru*.

Gizo was hit by an earthquake and tsunami in 2007. Many of the once-pristine reefs were devastated by the earthquake, leaving them looking like boulder fields. However, there is plenty of evidence of coral regrowth, and dive sites like Grand Central Station, Yellow Corner and Hotspot still offer some of the most extraordinary concentrations of reef fish on the planet.

On the uninhabited island of Tetepare, the single ecolodge is run by the Tetepare Descendants Association. Snorkelling trips often include sightings of Dugongs and Leatherback Turtles for the lucky swimmer. Jungle walks encounter massive Coconut Crabs (*Birgus*

Above: Sea fans (*Gorgonia* spp.) can provide a habitat for several types of cryptic fish, including pygmy seahorses.

Top: Despite their name, coconuts are not the main food of Coconut Crabs. They consume fruits, the pith of fallen trees and even carrion.

Above: Seaweed is collected and brought back to shore to be cleaned and dried for sale to make emulsifiers.

Top: Despite their fierce appearance Chevron Barracuda (*Sphyraena putnamae*) are generally harmless to divers.

latro), growing up to 1 m (3¼ ft) across from leg to leg; the crabs used to be common elsewhere but are rare now due to excessive hunting throughout their range. Diving resorts are scattered throughout Marovo Lagoon. At the northern end of the lagoon divers regularly encounter several species of shark patrolling the outer reefs and lagoon, as well as two species of manta ray at a well-known site where they aggregate for cleaning by smaller fish.

MANGROVES

Mangroves cover about 2 per cent of the Solomon Islands' land area, and provide food, timber and firewood to many coastal communities. The Mangrove Mud Shell (*Polymesoda erosa*) and Mud Crab are two of the most important food sources in mangroves, while the dense roots of the trees create a safe nursery area for many species of reef fish that can be caught when they mature.

The mangroves of the Solomon Islands, as elsewhere in the Coral Triangle, are being exploited beyond their capacity as human population pressures demand more firewood and construction material and land for agriculture. Impacts of climate change, including changes in rainfall, storm intensity and erosion, are also adversely impacting mangroves around the Solomon Islands. Most mangroves in the Solomon Islands fall within customary tenure regimes, and management responsibility lies with the customary owners. Outsiders are generally allowed to take small quantities of material from the forest, while larger harvests require the approval of the owners. However, as populations grow it is becoming harder and harder to enforce customary tenure.

LOCAL CHALLENGES

With so many coral reefs, mangroves, seagrasses and pelagic resources, the Solomon Islands are critical for the health of the Coral Triangle. The tensions of 1999–2001 led to the near-total collapse of the government until the Regional Assistance Mission to Solomon Islands restored security and some government functions. The government continues to rebuild its capacity to manage natural resources, but with a rural and relatively small population dispersed across many islands the challenges are enormous. Much of natural-resource management is left to traditional resource owners and customary practices. In some cases this has led to degradation of forests through logging contracts with foreign companies, and overfishing of some marine resources including sea cucumbers. However, as the vast majority of land and coastal waters is owned through the traditional clan and family-tenure systems, the potential for local management of resources is very high. This also leads to challenges of how to build capacity among so many coastal communities and how to deal with the erosion of some traditions as modern culture slowly infiltrates even the most remote areas.

NATIONAL PLAN *of* ACTION

IMPLEMENTATION of the Solomon Islands' National Plan of Action is jointly led by the Ministry of Environment, Conservation and Meteorology and the Ministry of Fisheries and Marine Resources. It is intended to be people centred with a goal to sustainably

> manage marine resources to ensure food security, sustainable economic development, biodiversity conservation and adaptation to emerging threats through community based resource management approaches supported by government agencies and other partners. (MECM/MFMR, 2010)

The national plan is designed to help implement policies set before the CTI, including the Coastal Community Strategy, revised Fisheries Act and National Biodiversity Strategy and Action Plan, while maintaining its focus on community management and support for livelihoods. One of the first steps for the national plan was to overcome the difficulty in building capacity for communities to manage resources over such a vast area. Geographic priorities were set for a first and subsequent phases of implementation based on needs, logistics and presence of partner organizations. As such, Malaita, Western and Central Provinces were set as the first priorities, with the others to come in a second phase of activity.

The Solomon Islands' plan differs significantly from those of the other CTI countries as it does not follow the five goals (seascapes, ecosystem approach to fisheries management, marine protected areas, threatened species, climate change adaptation) of the Regional Plan of Action (see page 33). The Solomons Islands' plan is centred on strengthening community-based natural-resource management through four main themes:

- Supporting community-based resource management.
- Developing policies, legislation, partnerships and strategies.
- Managing data for coordination and decision making.
- Education and awareness raising.

There are many manifestations of community-based resource management in the Solomon Islands. The Locally Managed Marine Area is one of the most commonly used tools. The Solomon Islands Locally Managed Marine Area Network was established in 2003 as a network of protected area and community-management practitioners who work to better manage coastal and marine resources. The network's mission is to:

help communities manage [and] conserve marine resources to maximize benefits and ensure food security by sourcing funds, facilitating, coordinating and providing information, building capacity and empowering partners through traditional and scientific approaches.

One of the main drawbacks of the traditional management systems was the lack of laws that articulated penalties and provided an avenue for prosecution when a community's protected area was violated. Within a community, enforcement would normally be managed by the community itself, but when outsiders encroached into a protected area, there was no legal recourse. A major development of marine-resource management was the passing, in 2010, of the national Protected Areas Act, and a set of Protected Area Regulations in 2012 to accompany the act. With these two pieces of legislation, communities can now legally register their protected area, enforce it and prosecute anyone who does not abide by the regulations.

One of the recent key activities for conservationists throughout the Solomon Islands was responding to this new legal avenue for enforcing protected areas. The new legislation provided a framework for developing and registering community-based management plans. Many communities, however, had no way of knowing the process for developing a management plan, or how to submit it to the government. To make the process easier, the Solomon Islands Public Defender's Office produced a guideline and series of templates for creating a government-endorsed, community-managed protected area.

The process includes several steps, such as extensive community consultations, the establishment of a management committee to draft the management plan, the submission to the government and an inspection by the government before the final signing of the document by the Minister of Environment and Conservation. The management plan should include a map of the area with clear boundaries that are agreed upon with neighbouring communities or tribes. If the boundary is disputed, the protected area cannot be created. The management plan must include a list of zones within the protected area and the restrictions on activities within each zone. Once the application is approved and signed by the minister, the plan becomes legally recognized and trespassers can be prosecuted.

Opposite: Banded Sea Kraits (*Laticauda colubrina*) possess one of the strongest venoms in the world, but rarely bite divers. They hunt for eels and small fish on dives that can last many minutes before they surface for air.

CONSERVATION INITIATIVES

INTERNATIONAL environmental NGOs, local NGOs and community groups are working with the Solomon Islands' government at the national, provincial and village levels to improve management of marine resources in the Solomon Islands. The national government relies on partners to help implement projects on the ground.

ARNAVON ISLANDS PROJECT

One of the longest running marine-conservation projects in the Solomon Islands is in the Arnavon Islands between the large islands of Choiseul and Santa Isabel. The Arnavons are a small group of three small islands in the narrow channel between the two big islands, and are important nesting beaches for the Hawksbill Turtle.

Hawksbill Turtles are found throughout the tropics. They are closely associated with coral reefs and use their sharp, hawk-like beaks to forage for sponges and other invertebrates among the

corals. Like other sea turtles, they spend their entire adult lives at sea, except when females return to the beach on which they hatched to lay new clutches of eggs every two to three years. Hawksbill Turtles are listed on the IUCN Red List of Threatened Species as Critically Endangered throughout their range. They require healthy coral reefs to survive, and the global decline of coral reefs is one of the biggest threats to them. Historically, they were hunted for their shells, which were used to make jewellery and other fashion accessories. Their eggs are collected for food and in some areas, including the Arnavon Islands, they are hunted for their meat.

There are three communities that claim traditional rights to the resources of the Arnavons. Kia and Katupika villages, on Santa Isabel and Choiseul respectively, shared the resources of the Arnavons for decades. In the late 1960s a group of people from the Gilbert Islands (now Kiribati) were resettled to nearby Waghena by the colonial British government. With the influx of this new group, the resources became contested as all three groups claimed rights. The communities use the islands for fishing, collecting the eggs of megapode birds and hunting Hawksbill Turtles. As the resources declined the government of the Solomon Islands banned the hunting of the turtles in the Arnavon Islands in the late 1980s. However, this was done without community consultation, and the ban was rejected and eventually withdrawn. Islanders even resorted to burning down the enforcement structure that the government built on one of the islands. The hunting continued until the mid-1990s.

In the early 1990s the government tried again to protect the turtles, but this time took a different approach. The American TNC was enlisted to help conduct surveys and engage with the three communities to discuss ways to manage the islands. By 1995 the communities had agreed to establish the Arnavon Community Marine Conservation Area with a management committee comprising village representatives, the provincial and federal governments, and TNC. The conservation area, set at 157 sq km (61 sq miles), was declared as a totally no-take area not just for turtles, but for all marine and land species within its boundaries. Key to this success is the structure of the management committee, and the inclusion of the three communities in setting the agenda of and managing the protected area.

The conservation area has worked to protect the turtles. Community members from the three villages take turns to patrol the area and collect data. Since its establishment the protected area has helped to increase the Hawksbill Turtle populations by 400 per cent. The tagging programme has shown that the turtles migrate as far as the Great Barrier Reef and New Caledonia to feed before returning to the Arnavons during the nesting season. Now the area has around 1,200 nests per year. There have also been increases in sea cucumbers, and reports that fishing around the boundaries has improved (J. Plotsky, *Home for Hawksbill* film, 2010).

By setting aside the Arnavon Islands as a conservation area, the communities lost an important source of income. There has been only mixed success with efforts to replace that income. In the late-1990s a fish-processing centre was established to help the local fishermen to freeze and sell their catches for export. However, the tensions of 1999 and the low price of fish made the centre unprofitable and it closed. Since then seaweed farming has been introduced to the villages, and some community members earn income from the low levels of tourism that the protected area attracts (United Nations Development Programme, 2012).

MALAITA PROJECTS

Malaita is the largest island of Malaita province. At 164 km (102 miles) long and just 37 km (23 miles) at its widest, it is a long, narrow land mass and has the Solomon Islands' largest population, estimated at more than 140,000 in 2013, over a sixth of the entire country. The population density has led to depletion of land and marine resources. The migration of people to urban areas of Malaita and the country's capital, Honiara, led to the ethnic violence that shook the Solomon Islands from 1999 to 2003. Partly because of the population density on the mainland, communities in Lau Lagoon, the north-east coast of Malaita, have built, and live upon, artificial islands made from blocks of coral mined from local reefs. The Lau Lagoon contains at least 60 artificial islands.

Malaita is also home to a community of dolphin hunters. Within some cultures of Malaita dolphin teeth are used as traditional currency, particularly for paying a bride's dowry. Fanalei is the most famous and active dolphin-hunting village. The hunt is conducted using an armada of up to 50 canoes manned by a single fisherman each. The boats deploy up to 10 km (6 miles) offshore, leaving 1–2 km (½–1 mile) between them, and wait for a pod of dolphins. Often the armada returns home without spotting any prey. When a pod is found, the fishermen communicate with multi-coloured flags attached to bamboo poles as they manoeuvre their boats into a U shape to corral the dolphins into a mangrove bay, where they are caught. The most common species to be caught in this way are Spinner Dolphins and Pantropical Spotted Dolphins (*Stenella attenuata*). The hunts generally happen only during a specific season, and up to 300 animals can be taken at one time. A dolphin-advocacy group, Earth Island Institute, attempted to compensate the villagers for not hunting dolphins and the practice was stopped for a few years starting in 2010, but it restarted again in 2013 when

a dispute arose about the nature of the payments or who should be receiving the funds.

With Malaita as one of the first-phase focal provinces for the CTI in the Solomon Islands, the WorldFish Centre conducted several programmes related to community-based management of mangroves and mangrove fisheries, as well as helping to introduce aquaculture to the island to offset declines in coastal fish populations.

At the southern end of Malaita, the Maramasike Passage is a narrow strip of water that separates North Malaita from South Malaita. There is no road access to the villages in the region, so access is exclusively by boat. Mangroves line the edges of the passage, and one village on South Malaita, Eliote, is the main home of the resource owners and users. These people make daily forays into the mangrove forests to collect fish, shellfish, wood and fruits for

Above: Dolphin teeth are an important part of the culture of the people of Malaita Island where they are used as shell money to pay bride prices.

Opposite: Tuna that are not fit for export are often sold in the markets of Honiara. The fish is an important export resource in the Solomon Islands and must be managed carefully.

daily consumption and to sell at distant markets. The demand for clams and crabs from Honiara has resulted in local depletions of the resources as villagers are using new and more efficient techniques to collect them (Albert & Schwarz, 2013).

A project completed by the WorldFish Centre in the Maramasike Passage attempted to demonstrate best practices for establishing community-management plans within the Solomon Islands' mangrove forests to ensure that resources are used sustainably and can adapt to the altering environmental regimes that come with a changing climate. The project built on some existing principles of community-based resource management, including a stipulation that projects should only begin when a genuine request from an entire community has been received, consultations with stakeholders show sincere interest at all levels, and agreements between the project and the community are documented in writing.

The WorldFish Centre's team made many trips to the Eliote community after getting the initial permissions to conduct the project. Each trip required a ferry from the capital to Malaita, then a five-hour trip in an open boat, and the team would stay for at least a week. After an initial investigative trip to identify issues, governance structures and the status of traditional knowledge, the team conducted focal group discussions with various people, including

groups of men, women, the youth and other users. Men, women and young people use the mangroves in different ways, so separating them during discussions allowed the team to understand the issues that each group faced without being dominated by another group. Maps of the resources and use patterns were made, and the community was prompted for ideas about how to better manage the area. Eventually the team assisted the community to form a management committee with representation from different user and clan groups.

In Maramasike Passage the management community included 20 representatives from four clans, local leaders, teachers and other user groups. Eventually the committee established a management area with rules based on traditional knowledge and the community discussions held previously. Rules included respect and continued use of traditional *tambu* areas (taboo areas when harvesting is limited for certain times), gear restrictions, catch limits and fully closed areas. The committee established restrictions on the sizes of clams to be harvested and prohibited the capture of crabs with eggs, as well as destructive fishing methods or even the use of nets to catch fish and crabs. Penalties for breaching the rules and a monitoring plan to keep track of clam and crab populations were established, with a monitoring group of local youth trained to conduct monitoring once a month (Albert, Siota & Harohau, 2013).

TETEPARE DESCENDANTS ASSOCIATION

Tetepare in the south-western part of Western Province is the largest uninhabited island in the South Pacific Ocean. The original inhabitants fled the island around 150 years ago, but nobody is sure why they left. After that the forests and fisheries were left untouched and the biodiversity flourished. When loggers threatened to move onto the island to cut down the pristine trees, the descendants of the original inhabitants exerted their traditional claim on the resources of the island, formed the Tetepare Descendants Association and developed a plan for conserving the island. It now remains in its pristine condition and has a single guest house, run by the descendants, which operates as an ecolodge.

Besides protecting the intact forests, the association established the Solomon Islands' largest marine protected area along the southern coast of the island, including its reefs and lagoons (Anonymous, n.d.). No fishing or collection of any organism is allowed within the protected area or its beaches. Two additional protected areas are opened and closed on an annual basis to help maintain fish and shellfish resources. The association employs rangers to patrol the protected area and collects data about the status of the reefs, fish and invertebrate populations on a regular basis (United Nations Development Programme, 2013).

The flagship species of Tetepare's marine ecosystem is the Critically Endangered, majestic Leatherback Turtle. The largest turtle in the world, this species can reach up to 3 m (10 ft) in length and weigh more than 900 kg (1,985 lb). It regularly migrates across the Pacific Ocean to the west coast of North America to reach feeding grounds rich with jellyfish. Pacific Ocean populations of Leatherback Turtles are on the brink of extinction, with only a few remaining nesting beaches in eastern Indonesia, Papua New Guinea and the Solomon Islands. The turtles are hunted for their meat, their eggs are collected by coastal communities for food and they are frequent victims of by-catch in drift-net fisheries. These threats have wiped out 80 per cent of the Western Pacific Leatherback population.

Tetepare has a 2 km (1¼ mile) beach that is used by 30–50 female Leatherbacks from September to April each year, and the Tetepare Descendants Association maintains constant foot patrols throughout the season to locate and protect nests, tag the adult females and monitor hatch rates. The neighbouring island of Rendova gets more Leatherback nests than Tetepare, but is not protected. The association established an incentive programme where villagers from Rendova receive a financial incentive for reporting a Leatherback nest, and a second incentive when the nest successfully hatches (Conant, Somma, Laurisen & Bibb, 2013).

GIZO'S PROTECTED AREAS

Capital of the Solomon Islands' Western Province, Gizo is in close proximity to several large lagoons with hundreds of reefs, seagrass beds and mangrove forests. It has one of the best-developed tourism industries in the Solomon Islands, with several island resorts and guest houses and restaurants in Gizo town itself. It has also been the base of much of WWF's Solomon Islands marine conservation work for several decades. WWF implemented many

Left: Leatherback Turtles migrate between the Coral Triangle and the coast of California on one of the world's greatest annual migrations.

Opposite: Pantropical Spotted Dolphins are one of the species hunted for their meat and teeth by communities in Malaita.

projects around Gizo, with mixed results. As is the case with many conservation projects in Melanesia, the criticism frequently revolved around early projects that put biodiversity ahead of the needs of local people, and failed to deliver on promises for income to be derived from conservation projects. Sometimes the promises were not fulfilled or the expectations of the community were raised unrealistically.

For the past decade WWF has had two main priorities in the Gizo area. Building a network of marine protected areas to improve community-based resource management was the first priority. The Gizo islands consist of the large island of Ghizo and 47 other small islands stretching 23 km (14 miles) from north-west to south-east, interspersed with barrier reefs, reef-filled lagoons, seagrass beds and mangrove forests. A 2004 rapid ecological expedition by TNC noted that Gizo's easternmost Njari Island had one of the world's highest concentrations of reef-fish species, with 279 recorded during a single dive at the site. The area is also famous for its Second World War wrecks and the presence of Kennedy Island, where John F. Kennedy and his patrol-boat crew took refuge after being sunk by a Japanese destroyer.

Gizo is unusual in the Solomon Islands because large areas of the land and sea were alienated by the colonial government and are not under direct community management or tenure. After a series of headhunting raids by New Georgians in the 19th century Gizo's population fled to neighbouring islands. When the colonial British arrived they found an uninhabited island and made it government land. There is also one of the Solomon Islands' two groups of Gilbert Island settlers who arrived in the 1960s.

Efforts to establish a network of protected areas began in 1998 with four sites selected because they were under government ownership. It soon became clear that the protected areas would be more effective if they were established in places that were owned and managed by local communities. The Gizo Marine Conservation Area was born. The effects of the political and social unrest in 1999–2003 delayed the development of the marine-conservation areas, but important lessons were learned. The alienated land is contested by the original landowners who had fled the New Georgia headhunters. Now the inhabitants are a rich mix of original islanders, Gilbertese and settlers from around other parts of the Solomon Islands.

Gradually, the community members decided that the Gizo Marine Conservation Area should not only protect biodiversity, but also contribute to their economic well-being. To reflect the change, the name was changed to the Gizo Environmental Livelihood Conservation Association. The association has a management committee comprising community leaders from each of the ten management areas that have been established around the Gizo islands. The management areas contain 15 multiple-use protected areas and eight areas permanently closed to any form of fishing or collection (Liligeto, 2013).

An important aspect of the protected areas in the Solomon Islands, and Gizo in particular, is the protection of fish-spawning sites. Many species of coral-reef fish reproduce through a process of broadcast spawning. The males and females aggregate at a particular place on the reef and release sperm and eggs into the water column to mix, fertilize and develop into larvae that will eventually settle somewhere with good habitat. This important ecological process is well known to local fishermen, and an entire population of fish can be killed if a group of fishermen targets the spawning aggregation and catches all the fish on a single night.

Groupers (Serranidae) are one of the top predators on Asian Pacific coral reefs, feeding on fish, invertebrates and cephalopods. Some individuals can grow to large sizes exceeding 1.9 m (6 ft) and 400 kg (882 lb). Most are considerably smaller but still reach sizes of 50 cm (1½ ft) to 1 m (3¼ ft). They can live for more than 20 years. Because they are large, long lived and aggregate to spawn, they are vulnerable to overfishing. Many species also change sex as they age, switching from female to male as the older dominant males die. The light, flaky flesh of groupers makes them a prized food fish and a particular delicacy in southern Chinese cuisine. In many parts of Southeast Asia they are overfished and rare on reefs, but in the Solomon Islands it is still possible to see large groupers on many reefs. This is a good sign of overall reef health.

Two of the objectives of the Gizo Environmental Livelihood Conservation Association protected areas are to maintain the reef health and to protect the spawning aggregations. In order to avoid the potential of losing an entire population in one fishing trip, some of the protected areas are placed specifically at known grouper spawning aggregations, and are then declared totally protected areas.

Since the beginnings of the marine-conservation efforts in Gizo, WWF and James Cook University have documented and monitored the spawning sites. Monitoring of three species, Brown-marbled, Camouflage and Squaretail Groupers (*Epinephelus fuscoguttatus, E. polyphekadio* and *Plectropomus areolatus*), revealed that the fish usually aggregate on a specific reef site, generally a promontory facing strong currents, several days before the new moon. The results of the surveys prompted several management recommendations, including banning the sale of grouper species in Gizo market for the week before the new moon to discourage fishermen from targeting the spawning sites (Hughes, Leve & Napao, n.d.).

Opposite: The fish market in Gizo before the new moon. There are many species on sale, but no groupers in keeping with the regulations.

Below: One of the biggest bony fish species on the reef, Giant Groupers (*Epinephelus lanceolatus*), can grow to over 2 m (6½ ft) in length.

WORK IN MAROVO LAGOON

This lagoon fringes the eastern sides of Western Province's New Georgia and Vangunu Islands, with Gatokae Island at the southern end. At approximately 700 sq km (270 sq miles), it is considered the world's largest and best example of a double barrier reef lagoon. Within the lagoon are hundreds of small islands, patch reefs, mangrove forests and seagrass beds. Together with Tetepare, the lagoon was nominated by the Solomon Islands government as a World Heritage Site listed by UNESCO. The combination of the lagoon's geological significance, some of the remaining intact forests on New Georgia and Vangunu, and Tetepare's status as the largest uninhabited island in the Pacific made it an attractive candidate for World Heritage Site status. It remains on the tentative list, perhaps because of some of the grave threats to Marovo Lagoon's ecosystem.

There are more than 60 villages along the length of the lagoon, with approximately 15,000 people. They have lived with the natural resources for centuries, but recent developments cast a shadow on the potential for continued sustainability. Logging operations on the large islands bordering Marovo have reportedly increased the sediment loads into the sea and smothered many areas of coral. Local communities report reduced water quality, reef and mangrove degradation, and a reduction in the fish they can catch. Many of the loggers come from foreign companies, particularly from Malaysia and Korea, and the camps are also blamed for social problems including prostitution and alcoholism.

The process for obtaining logging licenses in the Solomon Islands can be unclear, but it requires the approval of local landowners. Sometimes a few influential landowners are paid to sign over the rights to their land, but the rest of the community receives very little benefit and the sums paid are a tiny fraction of the value of the logs that are removed. Along with logging operations, some oil-palm plantations have been established around the lagoon. With these industries comes the potential for growing populations that will plant more gardens and increase the nutrient input to the lagoon through development and sewerage.

Run-off and nutrient inputs from land threaten the lagoon by smothering habitats and decreasing water quality through increased algal growth. For the waters of the lagoon to stay clear and allow the healthy growth of corals and seagrasses that underlie the integrity of the ecosystem the algae must be controlled. Without measures to control pollution entering the lagoon it is essential that herbivores, both fish and invertebrate, be allowed to thrive. If pollution is increased and herbivorous fish disappear, the result can be catastrophic.

Some herbivorous reef fish, including parrotfish and rabbitfish, are critical for keeping algae growing among the corals to a minimum. If these groups are overfished the algae can thrive on the nutrient pollution and quickly out-compete the slower growing corals. Some invertebrates, especially sea cucumbers, filter decaying material from the bottom sediments and play an important role in maintaining water quality. Fishing and processing of sea cucumbers is one of the main income sources for remote villages in the Solomon Islands and in many areas they are overfished. Several attempts to ban fishing for sea cucumbers throughout the Solomon Islands have proven to be controversial and difficult to enforce.

In accordance with the Solomon Islands' national policy on pursuing local community management, several projects are working to improve the management capacity of the communities in Marovo Lagoon. One group, the Marovo Island Natural Biodiversity and Livelihood Trust, is a local group that focuses on the resources and management by several communities on Marovo Island in the middle of the lagoon. The trust was established in 2006 to help the Chea, Sasaghana and Chubikopi communities on Marovo Island to reduce poverty, through protection and management of marine and terrestrial resources, by building their capacity to make decisions on how to manage their own resources. As part of the effort, the trust engages in developing management plans for the marine resources under their traditional jurisdiction, building alternative livelihood options for members of the community, and maintaining local traditions, culture and knowledge.

Left: The barrier reef of Marovo Lagoon's eastern edge is visible as a long, thin ribbon of reefs.

Opposite: Dusky Parrotfish (*Scarus niger*) have a large variation in colours across their range.

8

TIMOR LESTE

Timor Leste is the youngest country in the Coral Triangle and the smallest signatory to the CTI, with a land area of only 14,874 sq km (5,743 sq miles) and just over 700 km (435 miles) of coastline. It occupies the eastern half of Timor Island, shared with Indonesia. The exclave province of Oeccuse lies 60 km (37 miles) inside Indonesia, and Timor Leste citizens must obtain an Indonesian visa just to get there via the road through Indonesia. A rugged mountain range runs from east to west through the country and reaches a peak altitude of 2,963 m (9,721 ft). Coastal plains on the north and south coasts have a thin and rocky soil. The northern coast experiences a six-month dry season every year, while the southern coast gets more rain throughout the year.

Left: Large schools of Sleek Unicorn Fish (*Naso hexacanthus*) inhabit the passage between Jaco Island and mainland Timor to feed on plankton where the current flows most strongly.

TIMOR LESTE

Roma

BANDA SEA

Wetar

Kisar

Cape Acremo

Mau Meta

Atauro *Cape Eromalian*

Wetar Strait

Cape Laturo Vati

Com *Cape Tei*
Tutuala

Laivai *Jaco*

Baucau

Nino Konis Santana National Park

Alor

Vemasse

Liquiça

DILI

TIMOR LESTE

Lore

SAVU SEA

Batugade

Alimbata

Beasso
Cape Deilubun

Pante Macassar

Betano

TIMOR LESTE
OECUSSE

Beco

Cape Caetec

Suai

INDONESIA

200m
2000m
4000m

⊂⊃ Coral reefs

• Towns/cities

● National parks

TIMOR SEA

INDIAN OCEAN

0   30 Miles

0   60 Kilometres

Timor Leste was a colony of Portugal from the 16th century until 1975. The colony produced sandalwood, coffee and marble as major exports. The country is still recovering from the decades of violence that started nine days after it declared independence from Portugal when Indonesian military forces invaded in 1975. The ensuing struggle lasted until 1999, when a referendum voted for independence. In the weeks after the referendum militias fighting for continued Indonesian rule, supported by the Indonesian military, went on an orgy of destruction and wiped out much of the infrastructure, including schools, roads, government buildings and 100 per cent of the electrical grid. Hundreds of thousands of people fled as refugees. The violence only ended when a UN-backed peacekeeping force restored order. Another UN force was required in 2006, when law and order broke down again amid conflict within the military. The UN then helped rebuild the country until it officially withdrew in 2012.

The PEOPLE

MORE than 80 per cent of the nearly 1.1 million people rely on small-scale agriculture to survive. Due to its poor soil and inconsistent rainfall Timor Leste is a net importer of food. The two official languages are Portuguese and Tetum, but the society is multi-ethnic and there are at least 25 major languages. Many people understand Bahasa Indonesian as well. Timor Leste's per capital gross domestic product is estimated at US $10,000 per year, but that figure is misleading because of the country's offshore oil wealth in the Timor Sea, shared (and disputed) with Australia. The government established a fund to grow revenue from its oil exports. The fund stood at US $11.8 billion in 2012. One of the biggest debates within Timor Leste is how to spend the fund and what development projects are of the highest priority. It is telling that in 2010 Timor Leste ranked among the top three countries in the world for child malnutrition.

The literacy rate is the lowest in the Coral Triangle, with only 58 per cent adults able to read and write (CIA, 2012).

The constitution of Timor Leste recognizes the importance of a healthy and sustainable environment and the role of traditional culture in maintaining the environment. One of the objectives of the state is to 'protect the environment and preserve natural resources', while acknowledging that 'everyone has the right to a humane, healthy, and ecologically balanced environment' (McIntyre, 2011).

Above: The strait between Timor and Jaco Islands has strong currents that attract large schools of fish when the tide is coming in.

Opposite: At the far eastern tip of Timor Island, uninhabited Jaco Island is the largest in the Nino Konis Santana Park.

MARINE RESOURCES

TIMOR Leste's coast borders the Timor Sea, an arm of the Indian Ocean to the south, and the Savu Sea and Wetar Strait to the north. The Wetar Strait is a deep trench between Timor and the Indonesian islands of Alor and Wetar. The Timor Sea is a relatively shallow shelf sea between Timor and north-western Australia. A major part of the Indonesian Through-flow current enters the Indian Ocean at the eastern end of Timor. Timor Leste has only two islands, with Atauro in the Wetar Strait north of the capital, Dili, and Jako Island at the far eastern end of Timor.

Very few marine-resource surveys have examined the southern coast of Timor Leste and little is known about it. It has wider coastal plains and river deltas than the northern coast. Wave action and currents are stronger on the southern coast, resulting in fewer coral reefs, seagrasses and mangrove forests. The nutrient inputs from the rivers and the shallower sea are thought to contribute to the southern coast's greater fisheries production.

Most of the country's coral reefs are found along the northern coast. It is more thoroughly surveyed, and is characterized by narrow fringing reefs and steep drop-offs descending to hundreds of metres. There are several small areas of mangroves interspersed along the coast, but only 18 sq km (7 sq miles) of this habitat remain in Timor Leste compared with an estimated 90 sq km (35 sq miles) in the early 20th century.

Reliable estimates of fishing in Timor Leste are non-existent. There is no domestic commercial fishing industry, and most fishing activities are small in scale and limited to coastal areas. A few Indonesian-registered tuna long-liners venture into the Timor Sea on trips that can last for up to several weeks. There are less than 10,000 full-time fishermen in Timor Leste. Women and children in coastal communities exploit the reef flats during low tides to collect shellfish, octopus and other invertebrates for subsistence consumption (National CTI Coordinating Committe Timor Leste, 2012).

Right: Coastal communities in Timor Leste venture onto the fringing reef at low tide gleaning for small fish, shells and other invertebrates to eat or sell.

Opposite: After the war for independence many people in Timor Leste were left without good knowledge of the sea, but fishing is becoming an increasingly important livelihood.

MARINE MAMMALS

DESPITE the fact that Timor Leste has such a small marine area, its waters are home to a world-class array of marine mammals. Surveys conducted in 2008 identified at least 13 species of marine mammal around the coasts. The majority of sightings were on the northern coast, but huge schools of small marine mammals, probably feeding on squids, were sighted from time to time. Small pods of Pilot Whales (*Globicephala macrorhyncus*) and False Killer Whales (*Pseudorca crassidens*) are frequently encountered near the coast. Blue Whales and Sperm Whales use the Wetar Strait to enter and exit the Savu Sea to the west, possibly for feeding or migration (Dethmers et al., 2012).

DIVING

Tourism is largely undeveloped in Timor Leste, but there are some opportunities to explore the reefs through dive shops based in Dili. Some of the best dive spots for macro diving and cryptic creatures are found just in front of the Dili waterfront and port. Because many of the mainland reefs are coastal fringing reefs, beach dives are common. Just a few kilometres west of Dili, Dugongs are often sighted as divers enter and exit the water from the beach. The dive centres make frequent trips to Atauro Island to dive its spectacular walls. Massive schools of dolphins are often spotted in the channel between Dili and Atauro.

The Nino Konis Santana National Park (see also page 201) at the eastern tip of the island is nearly pristine. A 2012 survey of Timor Leste's reefs conducted by Conservation International with the government of Timor Leste found that the healthiest reefs were mostly found within the park (Erdmann & Mohan, 2013). Big walls, sandy plains and healthy corals await intrepid divers. Fields of Garden Eels (*Heteroconger hassi*) in the deep give way to huge sting rays, reef sharks, and schools of unicorn fish and snappers in the channel between uninhabited Jaco Island and the mainland. There are no diving facilities near the park, so all diving trips must be arranged from Dili. Local communities can arrange for snorkelling trips to Jaco Island or nearby reefs, but they do not have any equipment for hire.

Above: Giant Clams (*Tridacna gigas*) are cultured in many parts of the Coral Triangle in an effort to restock them on to reefs. Wild individuals, such as this one in Nino Konis Santana National Park, are rare.

Left: The Porcelain Crab (*Neopetrolisthes maculatus*) lives deep within the tentacles of certain species of anemone.

Opposite: Cup corals decorate an overhang at Jaco Island.

THREATS *to* MARINE RESOURCES

TIMOR Leste has a relatively small population, but rapid growth rates of both population and incomes. A fast increase of both can threaten marine resources as people with few employment options turn to the sea to meet daily nutrition and income needs. Throughout the Coral Triangle rapid population growth is associated with loss of marine resources and degradation of habitats. Timor Leste has not reached this point yet, but it is a grave concern.

There are few reports of destructive fishing in Timor Leste. Some communities utilize the derris vine to poison fish on the reefs. Blast fishing was employed during the Indonesian occupation, and occasional trips by illegal fishermen from Indonesia are known to use the method, but it is not commonly employed by local fishermen.

Many of the reefs along the north-west coast of Timor Leste show evidence of sedimentation. With very few alternatives, local communities turn to their forests for cooking fuel and building materials. On the hills along the north-west coast uncontrolled harvesting and overharvesting of timber, for cooking fuel and building material, leads to erosion of topsoil that eventually and inevitably ends up on coral reefs. The accumulation of this sediment has smothered and devastated large areas of coral reef. The eastern end of the island has more intact forests and does not yet show the impacts of sedimentation.

Right: Mushroom Corals (*Fungiidae* spp.) can often be found in large concentrations across the reef.

Opposite: The waters of Nino Konis Santana National Park can be extremely clear and full of schools of fish.

NATIONAL PLAN *of* ACTION

TIMOR Leste's National Plan of Action for the Coral Triangle was published in 2009 by the Secretary of State for Fisheries and Aquaculture in the Ministry of Agriculture and Aquaculture. The plan makes clear at the very beginning that it aligns closely with existing policies, plans and projects of the government of Timor Leste, developed through a process of stakeholder consultation and meetings with partners. It also explicitly states that the plan was developed internally and is not driven by external plans, agendas or development models.

The plan follows the Regional Plan of Action's five goals (see page 33), but includes independent actions towards each goal. These focus primarily on studies and establishing necessary legislation to protect the coastal and marine environment. As a young country, Timor Leste still lacks many necessary laws and regulations to conduct marine conservation and resource management. The emphasis on studies reflects the general lack of information and knowledge about Timor Leste's marine environment, which hampers marine-resource management.

Timor Leste's goal of implementing an Ecosystem Approach to Fisheries Management differs from the regional plan. The country's plan includes two targets.

- Developing data collection and management systems so that resource managers can know what marine resources exist in the country and understand the status of resource health. This includes surveys of how much effort fishermen put into catching fish (hours at sea, number of boats, and so on) and fish stocks.
- Poverty-reduction projects that might incorporate integrated coastal management and ecosystem management of fisheries. Such projects include testing community-based fishery-management projects, developing a national aquaculture strategy and providing alternative income-generating mechanisms to poor coastal communities.

Ecosystem approach to fisheries management

Managing fisheries is a challenging task under the best conditions. Fish are hidden under the surface of the sea, constantly move around, often travelling great distances, and populations fluctuate naturally. Understanding how many fish there are, how they reproduce and what they need to survive is the task of fisheries scientists. Fisheries managers are responsible for determining how many fish can be caught, by whom, when, where and with what gear. For many decades fisheries scientists and managers have attempted to determine the 'maximum sustainable yield' of any fishery by calculating how fish reproduce and how many can be caught to ensure that the population does not decline. In many cases they have been wrong. In other cases fishing lobbies and politics have conspired to undermine the scientists. In addition, until recently the fish were managed without considering the habitats in which they live.

A relatively new paradigm for fisheries management, advocated by the CTI, is attempting to change how managers approach the issue and to reverse the trend of declining fish populations. The new approach, often called an 'ecosystem approach to fisheries management', is purported to be more holistic than conventional management as it includes ecological well-being among its key areas of focus.

Across the region the fisheries are in decline. Populations of highly valued fish are dwindling, the average size of fish landed on boats is going down, and fishermen have to work harder and harder to catch the same amount of fish that their grandfathers caught. The total biomass of demeral fish, those trawled from the seabed, in Malaysia declined to between 43 and 96 per cent (depending upon the area) in just 30 years of commercial fishing. Surveyed bays in the Philippines showed similar declines. Papua New Guinea and the Solomon Islands have put a complete moratorium on sea cucumber fishing because of the dramatic declines in populations.

An ecosystem approach has objectives that go beyond the traditional ones of landing more fish and increasing income. New objectives relate to maintaining fish stocks, prey species and the habitats on which they depend. They also include more tools compared to conventional fisheries management that relied on limiting fishing effort by licensing fishermen, boats and gear, sometimes set quotas for the total amount of fish that could be taken and sometimes zoned certain areas to reduce conflict between different types of fishing. In addition to conventional interventions, the ecosystem approach employs zoning for ecological considerations, the use of marine protected areas and market-based incentives to achieve sustainability. Importantly, definitions of the ecosystem approach often include humans as part of the ecosystem and broaden the spectrum of stakeholders involved in the management process. It encourages managers to engage not only with the fishing industry but also with other industries, including shipping, oil and gas exploration, and tourism. Encouraging such cooperation is critical for maintaining the integrity of the seas.

As populations grow, climate changes and stresses on the marine environment mount, promoting the natural capacity of the marine ecosystem to bounce back from perturbations can be a major outcome of a well-planned and implemented ecosystem approach. Fisheries managers often have to make decisions with insufficient data and may choose to err on the side of caution to promote ecosystem well-being. Most challenging would be the willingness of managers to adapt their management techniques as circumstances change and new information is obtained. Sometimes managers may feel that the reversal of a decision or the updating of a regulation can be seen as a failure of the original decision, but adapting to new circumstances is not a failure of decision making, rather it is a critical component of ensuring the health of our seas.

The regional plan calls for the increased use of marine protected areas for marine conservation and sustainable resource management, and that call is acknowledged in the Timor Leste plan. The major difference is that Timor Leste's plan focuses on the role that protected areas may play in 'natural asset management' while maintaining a balance between protecting nature, and ensuring that there are avenues for job creation and improving the capacity of communities to engage in natural-resource management. As of 2014 Timor Leste has three official marine protected areas, including the large Nino Konis Santana National Park, and two smaller protected areas at Atauro Island and Batugade.

For the final goal, Timor Leste planned to assess the costs and benefits of signing on to CITES and the Ramsar Convention on Wetlands, and joining the IUCN. Joining CITES requires that members assess the impact that international trade will have on endangered species, and establish a quota system for species listed in the treaty, or banning all trade of those listed as most endangered. The plan also called for legislation on protected and endangered species.

NINO KONIS SANTANA PARK

THE Nino Konis Santana National Park occupies the eastern tip of the island, Jaco Island and 55,600 ha (137,391 acres) of marine area, including coral reefs, seagrass beds and mangroves. The park is named after a hero of the struggle for independence, Jose Conisso Antonio Santana – better known as Nino Konis Santana – who came from the region now protected by the park. The park protects some of the best remaining forest on Timor Island, containing many important bird areas and cultural sites, including ancient cave paintings that date back 40,000 years.

The park is home to several communities and is classified as an IUCN category V park – a protected seascape and landscape. This designation recognizes and values the interactions between people and the environment, and allows for cultural aspects of the local communities to be maintained while protecting the biodiversity and natural values of the area. The park was officially designated in 2007, only five years after independence, but the area had enjoyed special status under Indonesian and UN-led governments. The specific aims of the park include protection and conservation, but are heavily weighted towards the rights and customs of local people and the need for sustainable development in the area.

As a young and relatively poor country, Timor Leste faces particular challenges in managing coastal resources. Several challenges to effective management of the park were identified in 2009. At that time many of the government staff lacked experience or necessary knowledge to manage a protected area. There are also problems with basic infrastructure, including the poor roads along the northern coast linking the protected area with the capital, Dili. There are only two ways to reach Com, the closest coastal town in the park, from Dili. It is possible to arrange for a private tour with car and driver from Dili, or choose to use local transportation.

Local transportation comprises an eight-hour journey in a series of buses navigating the coastal road along cliffs soaring over the reefs and sea below, and descending to several coastal towns along the way. Travellers need to get to the bus stop early and try for a good seat near the window. Latecomers have to sit on the floor of the aisle, stand in the open doorway or even ride on the roof of the bus. Travellers to Com can choose to stay overnight in Baucau, East Timor's second largest town on a bluff overlooking the Wetar Strait. The bus stop in Baucau is an old wall in the shade of several massive banyan trees at the foot of the historic Pousada de Baucau

Left: Soft corals provide shelter for many species of juvenile fish.

Opposite: A man sells fish and turtle eggs from the back of his bicycle in Timor Leste's capital, Dili.

Hotel. From Baucau, the bus drops Com passengers in the tiny hamlet of Lautem, where the road passes through the centre of an ancient and crumbling Portuguese fort. The final two-hour stretch of the journey is on a hard wooden plank in the back of a pick-up truck, before being dropped in Com where one hotel and several guesthouses await.

As is the case with protected areas around the world, sustainable financing to manage the area is lacking in Timor Leste. Sustainable ecotourism is one proposed mechanism in the park, but with only 51,000 arrivals at Dili's international airport in 2011, tourism is still not a significant income generator for the park. Because the park is intended to build upon traditions of customary tenure and community management, there is a need to build capacity among local communities. With low levels of education and significant communication barriers because the local language in Com differs from Tetum Dili (the language spoken in Dili and its surroundings), engaging local communities to manage the park poses several challenges (McIntyre, 2011).

Two NGOs, the Haburas Foundation and Conservation International, are working with the government and local communities to develop management plans and capacity to manage the park. The Haburas Foundation, established by one of Timor Leste's prominent freedom fighters, helps the six communities inside the park to incorporate their traditions and cultures into the management of the parks, and to engage with government officials to manage the park. The Haburas Foundation also works with communities to help them decide which aspects of their culture may be commercialized for tourism, and which parts they want to keep private. In Com, several community-run guesthouses were established to help bring ecotourism income to the local community. For marine conservation, Haburas works with three coastal communities, Com, Tutuala and Lore. Conservation International focuses on conducting marine surveys, developing a zoning and management plan for the park in consultation with resource users, and developing enforcement capacity.

Designating and enforcing zoning is a key tool for managing marine protected areas. Within a marine protected area some site zones may be completely closed to fishing, while other areas are designated diving sites or fishing areas for authorized local community members. Conservation International worked with the three coastal communities to establish three zones in the park that would be off limits to all fishing and collection of organisms. In theory these areas would also act as refugia for fish and shellfish to grow larger and reproduce, thus providing resources to fishermen nearby.

Each community designated an area near its village to set aside. In Com, the no-take area was established next to the village harbour, and fishermen had to pass the area on their way to and from their fishing grounds, thus making it easy to monitor if anybody was encroaching into the zone. The no-take zone for the Lore community was established quite far from it, so a patrol post was constructed where people could store equipment and seek shelter while monitoring. The Tutuala community is located high on a bluff overlooking the eastern tip of Timor Island and neighbouring Jaco Island, making monitoring relatively simple.

In each community a group of volunteers was trained to survey reefs and seagrasses. These volunteers form the core of a community-based management group for the park and the no-take zones. A big challenge for all the communities is enforcement. In early 2013 the community in Com could only watch as a group of illegal fishermen came and collected shells from within its no-take reserve. There is no official enforcement officer based in Com, and the community feared that the illegal fishermen might resort to violence if confronted. The national government is unable to prioritize fund allocation for park management while having to make other development decisions to build roads and ensure an adequate food supply for its people. This means that the future of the park currently depends heavily on the efforts of conservation groups to bring projects and project funds to support monitoring, enforcement and continued awareness projects as local communities search for ways to make the park profitable and sustainable.

The park and the associated no-take zones, along with the other marine protected areas recently established in Timor Leste, can help to ensure that the country's seas provide nutritional and revenue benefits through tourism long into the future. The question remains how does such a young country, with so many needs, determine which needs come first, and where to spend its limited but essential oil wealth?

Above: Local communities are permitted to fish within the boundaries of Nino Konis Santana Park but must help to patrol the agreed no-take areas.

Conclusion

Governments have the dual task of developing their economies while providing a clean and healthy environment for people. In the recent past this was seen as a war between two opposing forces. In some countries of the Coral Triangle, non-governmental organizations are seen by governments as a critical component of implementing policies because they have a better connection to communities on the ground. But when conservationists oppose the policies of a government it can become a difficult situation. In the Coral Triangle some choose to confront governments head on, while others prefer to work behind the scenes to make changes to policy and influence how it is implemented.

At one time commercial activity and development were to always be opposed. The picture has changed in recent decades. Corporations often have more resources than national governments and their decisions on sustainability can have a greater impact than a new government policy. Once consumers are demanding safer, cleaner products that do not damage the environment, companies will respond. Within the Coral Triangle campaigns to raise awareness about seafood sustainability issues are gaining strength in the Philippines, Indonesia and Malaysia. Governments are responding to calls for banning shark finning and other consumer campaigns. A concerned society, consumer associations and stricter labelling policies are the key to keeping this trend real.

Across the Coral Triangle environmentalists, including large and small NGOs, are working tirelessly to promote better practices of environmental stewardship with governments, the private sector and communities. Every government in the Coral Triangle has stressed that marine conservation cannot come at the expense of human well-being, and that livelihoods are a key indicator of success in conserving the Coral Triangle. Conservation cannot be only a luxury of rich people living far away from the problems. Divers who spend thousands and thousands of dollars on gear and travel often arrive on a poor, remote island for a nice holiday and expect untouched reefs. The poor fisherman who lives on that island sees the coral reef as a livelihood and as a way to feed his family.

Protected areas and new fisheries regulations can only be successful if they have the support of local communities. Support can be achieved through respect, consultation and ensuring that communities are not burdened by conservation measures. There is also a need for additional political will and motivation across the Coral Triangle for a healthy environment. When politicians know that their constituencies value a clean and functioning environment, they will make decisions that reflect those values.

The Coral Triangle Initiative for Coral Reefs, Fisheries and Food Security is just one of many international agreements that the countries of the Coral Triangle have signed to protect the environment. It is significant because it grew out of the region itself. The agreement captures the most pressing issues to be addressed by 2020. It can be argued that all the countries' governments, NGOs and people could be doing more to achieve the goals, but the challenges are massive. We must remain optimistic that we can succeed, but we must also keep a realistic viewpoint and know that the struggle will go on long beyond the target date of 2020.

Below: Clownfish live symbiotically with several species of anemone. The fish has a safe place to brood its eggs while helping to keep parasites from the anemone and perhaps acting as a lure to attract prey to its tentacles.

REFERENCES

Agostini, V. N., Grantham, H. S., Wilson, J., Mangubhai, S., Rotinsulu, C., Hidayat, N., Muljadi, A., Muhajir, Mongdong, M., Darmawan, A., Rumetna, L., Erdmann, M. V. & Possingham, H. P. (2012). *Achieving Fisheries and Conservation Objectives Within Marine Protected Areas: Zoning the Raja Ampat Network* (p. 74). The Nature Conservancy, Indo-Pacific Division. Denpasar.

Ahmad, A. T., Isa, M. M., Ismail, M. S. & Yusof, S. (2003). Status of Demersal Fishery Resources of Malaysia. In V. C. and D. P. G. Silvestre, L. Garces, I. Stobutzki, M. Ahmed, R. A. Valmonte-Santos, C. Luna, L. Lachica-Aliño & P. Munro (ed.), Management and Future Directions for Coastal Fisheries in Asian Countries. *WorldFish Center Conference Proceedings* 67, pp. 83–136.

Albert, J. & Schwarz, A. (2013). *Mangrove Management in Solomon Islands: Case Studies from Malaita Province* (p. 7). WorldFish Centre. Penang, Malaysia.

Albert, J., Siota, F. & Harohau, D. (2013). *Mangrove Ecosystem for Climate Change and Livelihood Solomon Islands (MESCAL-SI)*. Draft Final Report: Methodology and Lessons Learned During the Facilitation of Mangrove Resource Management at the MESCAL-SI Demonstration Site (p. 13). Worldish Centre. Honiara, Solomon Islands.

Allain, V., Kerandel, J.-A., Andréfouët, S., Magron, F., Clark, M., Kirby, D. S. & Muller-Karger, F. E. (2008). Enhanced Seamount Location Database for the Western and Central Pacific Ocean: Screening and Cross-checking of 20 Existing Datasets. *Deep Sea Research Part I: Oceanographic Research Papers* 55 (8), pp. 1035–47.

Allen, G. R. & Adrim, M. (2003). Coral Reef Fishes of Indonesia. *Zoological Studies* 42 (1), pp. 1–72.

Allen, G. & Steene, R. (2002). *Indo-Pacific Coral Reef Field Guide* (7th edn, p. 378). Tropical Reef Research. Singapore.

Almany, G. R, Hamilton, Richard J., Bode, M., Matawai, M., Potuku, T., Saenz-Agudelo, P., Planes, S., Berumen, M. L., Rhodes, K. L., Thorrold, S. R., Russ, G. R. & Jones, G. P. (2013). Dispersal of Grouper Larvae Drives Local Resource Sharing in a Coral Reef Fishery. *Current Biology* 23 (7), pp. 626–30.

Alonso, L. E., Deichmann, J. L., Mckenna, S. A., Naskrecki, P. & Richards, S. J. (2011). *Still Counting ...: Biodiversity Exploration for Conservation – The First 20 Years of the RAP Program* (p. 316). Conservation International. Arlington, Virginia.

Anonymous (2014). Protecting a Turtle Paradise in Indonesia. Accessed 15 May 2014 from www.worldwildlife. org/stories/protecting-a-turtle-paradise-in-indonesia

Anonymous (n.d.). Tetepare Descendants' Association. Accessed 8 April 2014 from www.tetepare.org

Arnold, M. & Fogarty, N. (2009). Reticulate Evolution and Marine Organisms: The Final Frontier. *International Journal of Molecular Sciences* 10 (9), pp. 3836–60.

Australian Institute of Marine Science (2014). *Evolution of Species*. AIMS Coral Fact Sheets. Accessed 14 January 2014 from http://coral.aims.gov.au/info/evolution-species.jsp

Barber, P., Palumbi, S., Erdmann, M. & Moosa, M. K. (2000). A Marine Wallace's Line? *Nature* 406 (August), pp. 692–3.

Bureau of Fisheries and Aquatic Resources (2011). *Philippine Fisheries Profile* (p. 36). Quezon City, Philippines.

Burke, L., Reytar, K., Spalding, M. & Perry, A. (2012). *Reefs at Risk Revisited in the Coral Triangle* (p. 86). World Resources Institute. Washington DC.

Carpenter, K. E. & Springer, V. G. (2005). The Center of the Center of Marine Shore Fish Biodiversity: The Philippine Islands. *Environmental Biology of Fishes* 72 (4), pp. 467–80.

Carter, E., Soemodinoto, A. & White, A. (2010). *Guide for Improving Marine Protected Area Management Effectiveness in Indonesia* (p. 60). The Nature Conservancy Indonesia Program. Bali, Indonesia.

Chan, E. (2006). Marine Turtles in Malaysia: On the Verge of Extinction? *Aquatic Ecosystem Health and Management* 9 (2), pp. 175–84.

CIA (2012). *World Fact Book*. Central Intelligence Agency. Washington DC.

Cinner, J., Marnane, M., McClanahan, T. R. & Almany, G. R. (2005), Periodic Closures as Adaptive Coral Reef Management in the Indo-Pacific. *Ecology and Society* 11. www.ecologyandsociety.org/vol11/iss1/art31/

Conant, T., Somma, A., Laurisen, A. M. & Bibb, K. (2013). *Leatherback Sea Turtle* (Dermochelys coriacea) *5-year Review: Summary and Evaluation* (p. 93). National Marine Fisheries Service and US Fish and Wildlife Service.

Conservation International (2011). Kalabia: Berlayar Sambil Belajar. Conservation International. Indonesia. www.youtube.com/watch?v=sD8-ftGlako

Coral Triangle Initiative (2012). *State of the Coral Triangle Highlights: Philippines* (p. 4). Manila.

Coral Triangle Initiative (2012). *State of the Coral Triangle Report Highlights: Malaysia* (p. 4). Kuala Lumpur.

Coral Triangle Initiative on Coral Reefs, Fisheries, and F. S. (CTI-CFF) (2009). *Regional Plan of Action, Coral Triangle Initiative on Coral Reefs, Fisheries and Food Security* (CTI-CFF) (p. 42). Manado.

Coral Triangle Initiative on Coral Reefs, Fisheries, and Food Security (CTI-CFF) (2013). *Coral Triangle Marine Protected Area System Framework and Action Plan* (p. 75). Cebu City, Philippines.

Costanza, R., D'Arge, R., de Groot, R., Farber, S., Grasso, M., Hannon, B., Limburg, K., Naeem, S., O'Neill, R. V., Paruelo, J., Raskin, R. G., Sutton, P. & van den Belt, M. (1997). The Value of the World's Ecosystem Services and Natural Capital. *Nature* 387 (6630), pp. 253–60.

De Goeij, J. M., van Oevelen, D., Vermeij, M. J., Osinga, R., Middelburg, J. J., de Goeij, A. F. P. M. & Admiraal, W. (2013). Surviving in a Marine Desert: The Sponge Loop Retains Resources Within Coral Reefs. *Science* 342 (6154), pp. 108–10.

Dethmers, K., Chatto, R., Meekan, M., Amaral, A. L., Cunha, C. B. de, Carvalho, N. A. de & Edyvane, K. (2012). *Marine Megafauna Surveys in Timor Leste: Identifying Opportunities for Potential Ecotourism – Final Report*. Project 3 of the Timor Leste Coastal-Marine

Habitat Mapping, Tourism and Fisheries Development Project (p. 42).

Dirhamsyah, Subijanto, J, Susanto, H. A., Nurhakim, S., Amin, I., Napitupulu, L., Timotius, S., Nurlaili, Damayanti, E., Yudiarso, P., Wen, Wen, Alhanif, R., Buriarto, A. & Kushardanto, H. (2012). *The State of the Coral Triangle in Indonesia: Coral Triangle Marine Resources: Their Status, Economies and Management* (p. 218). Jakarta, Indonesia.

Dygico, M. (2006). *Tubbataha Reefs: A Marine Protected Area That Works. A Case Study on the Philippines* (p. 22). WWF-Philippines. Quezon City, Philippines.

Ecott, T. (2002). *Onder water: Avonturen in een vloeibare wereld* (1st edn, p. 312). Prometheus. Amsterdam.

Erdmann, M. V. & Mohan, C. (2013). A Rapid Marine Biological Assessment of Timor-Leste, *RAP Bulletin of Biological Assessment. Conservation International* 66 (p. 166). Dili.

FAO (2013). Indonesia, FAO to Strengthen Fisheries and Aquaculture Cooperation. Accessed 28 May 2014 from www.fao.org/news/story/en/item/176776/icode

Foale, S. (2001). 'Where's our development?' Landowner Aspirations and Environmentalist Agendas in Western Solomon Islands. *The Asia Pacific Journal of Anthropology* 2 (2), pp. 44–65.

Goltenboth, F., Timotius, K., Milan, P. P. & Margraf, J. (2006). *The Ecology of Insular Southeast Asia: The Indonesian Archipelago* (p. 560). Elsevier. Amsterdam.

Green, A., Lokani, P., Atu, W., Ramohia, P., Thomas, P. & Almany, J. (2006). *Solomon Islands Marine Assessment: Technical Report of Survey Conducted May 13 to June 17, 2004*. TNC Pacific Countries Report No. 1/06.

Green, A., Lokani, P., Sheppard, S., Almany, J., Keu, S., Aitsi, J., Karvon, J. W., Hamilton, R. & Lipsett-moore, G. (2007). *Scientific Design of a Resilient Network of Marine Protected Areas Kimbe Bay, West New Britain, Papua New Guinea* (p. 73). TNC Pacific Island Countries Report No. 2/07.

Hamilton, R., Green, A. & Almany, J. (2009). *Rapid Ecological Assessment: Northern Bismarck Sea, Papua New Guinea. Technical Report of Survey Conducted August 13 to September 7, 2006* (p. 170). TNC Pacific Island Countries Report No. 1/09.

Hoegh-Guldberg, O., Hoegh-Guldberg, H., Veron, J. E. N., Green, A., Gomez, E. D., Lough, J., King, M., Ambariyanto, Hansen, L., Cinner, J., Dews, G., Russ, G., Schuttenberg, H. Z., Peñaflor, E. L., Eakin, C. M., Christensen, T. R. L., Abbey, M., Areki, F., Kosaka, R. A., Tewfik, A. & Oliver, J. (2009). *The Coral Triangle and Climate Change: Ecosystems, People and Societies At Risk* (p. 276). WWF Australia. Brisbane.

Hoeksema, B. W. (2007). *Delineation of the Indo-Malayan Centre of Maximum Marine Biodiversity: The Coral Triangle* in Biogeography, Time and Place: Distributions, Barriers and Islands. W Renema (ed.), pp 117-178, Springer. Dordrecht, The Netherlands.

Hogarth, P. (2007). *The Biology of Mangroves and Seagrass* (p. 284). Oxford University Press. Oxford.

Huffard C. L., Erdmann, M. V. & Gunawan, T. R. P. (2012). *Geographic Priorities for Marine Biodiversity Conservation in Indonesia* (p. 134). Ministry of Marine Affairs and Fisheries and Marine Protected Areas Governance Program, Jakarta.

Huffard, C. L., Wilson, J., Hitipeuw, C., Rotinsulu, C., Mangubhai, S., Erdmann, M. V., Adnyana, W., Barber, P., Manuputty, J., Mondong, M., Purba, G., Rhodes, K. & Toha, H. (2012). *Ecosystem Based Management in the Bird's Head Seascape Indonesia: Turning Science Into Action* (p. 40). Ecosystem Based Management Program: Conservation International, The Nature Conservancy and WWF Indonesia.

Hughes, A., Leve, T. & Napao, R. (n.d.). *Project Summary: Fish Spawning Aggregation* (p. 12). WWF-International Western Melanesia Programme. Gizo, Solomon Islands.

Kartawijaya, T. (2014). *Surf, Lobster and Tuna: Lombok's Bumbang Bay to Become Recreational Park*. Wildlife Conservation Society Indonesia Programme Marine Newsletter. http://programs.wcs.org/indonesia/Initiatives/Marine.aspx#

Khan, B. (2014). *Indonesia Oceanic Cetacean Program*. APEX International. Accessed 15 February 2014 from www.apex-environmental.com/IOCP.html

Kinch, J. (2010). *Integrated Coastal and Marine Resource Management in Papua New Guinea: A Review of Lessons and Best Practices* (pp. 1–39). Secretariat of the Pacific Regional Environment Program. Apia.

Liligeto, W. (2013). *Gizo Environment Livelihood Conservation Association (GELCA) Resource Management Plan* (p. 54). WWF Solomon Islands and Coral Triangle Support Partnership. Gizo, Solomon Islands.

Longhurst, A. (2007). *Ecological Geography of the Sea* (p. 558). Elsevier. Amsterdam.

Mangubhai, S. (2012). Local Communities in Raja Ampat Embrace MPA Zoning Plan. *Coral Triangle Initiative on Coral Reefs, Fisheries and Food Security*. Accessed 3 June 2014 from www.coraltriangleinitiative.org/news/local-communities-raja-ampat-embrace-mpa-zoning-plan

Marshall, N. J. (2000). Communication and Camouflage with the Same 'Bright' Colours in Reef Fishes. *Philosophical Transactions of the Royal Society of London. Series B, Biological Sciences* 355 (1401), pp. 1243–8.

McIntyre, M. A. (2011). *Capacity Development Action Plan for the Programme of Works on Protected Areas, Part 1 Situation Analysis, Timor Leste 2011*. Prepared for the Department of Protected Areas and National Parks, Ministry of Agriculture and Fisheries, Government of Timor Leste with assistance of United Nations Development Program, Timor-Leste and the Global Environment Facility. Landsborough, Queensland, Australia.

McKenzie, L. (2008). *Seagrass Educators Handbook* (p. 20). Seagrass Watch.

MECM/MFMR (2010). *Solomon Islands Coral Triangle Initiative National Plan of Action* (p. 61). Honiara, Solomon Islands.

Melick, D., Kinch, J. & Govan, H. (2012). How Global Biodiversity Targets Risk Becoming Counterproductive: The Case of Papua New Guinea. *Conservation and Society* 10 (4), p. 344.

Miththapala S. *Tidal Flats: Coastal Ecosystems Series*. Vol. 5. IUCN 2013. Colombo, Sri Lanka.

Muttaqin, E. & Campbell, S. (2014). Mutualism in Action: How WCS Promoted Co-management and Incentives to Boost Marine Biodiversity in Karimunjawa. *WCS-IP Marine Newsletter*. Accessed 1 June 2014 from http://indonesia.wcs.org/AboutUs/LatestNews/tabid/6824/articleType/ArticleView/articleId/1061/Mutualism-in-action-How-WCS-promoted-co-management-and-incentives-to-boost-marine-biodiversity-in-Karimunjawa.aspx

National CTI Coordinating Committe Timor Leste (2012). *State of the Coral Reefs of Timor Leste: Coral Triangle Marine Resources: Their Status, Economies and Management* (p. 39). Dili.

National Oceanography Directorate (2011). *Malaysia National Plan of Action: Coral Triangle Initiative* (p. 111). Putrajaya, Malaysia.

O'Dor, R., Miloslavich, P. & Yarincik, K. (2010). *Marine Biodiversity and Biogeography – Regional Comparisons of Global Issues, An Introduction*. PloS One 5 (8).

Olson, D. & Dinerstein, E. (1998). The Global 200: A Representation Approach to Conserving the Earth's Most Biologically Valuable Ecoregions. *Conservation Biology* 12 (3).

Orth, R., Carruthers, T. & Dennison, W. (2006). A Global Crisis for Seagrass Ecosystems. *Bioscience* 56 (12), pp. 987–96.

Pauly, D., Christensen, V. & Dalsgaard, J. (1998). *Fishing Down Marine Food Webs*. Science, vol. 279. (5352), pp. 860-3.

Pauly, D. & Froese, R. (2012). Comments on FAO's State of Fisheries and Aquaculture, or 'SOFIA 2010'. *Marine Policy* 36 (3), pp. 746–52.

Pine, R. (2007). *Donsol: Whale Shark Tourism and Coastal Resource Management. A Case Study on the Philippines* (p. 39). WWF-Philippines. Manila.

Pitcher, T., Morato, T., Hart, P. & Clark, M. (2007). *Seamounts: Ecology, Fisheries and Conservation* (p. 555). Blackwell Publishing. Oxford.

Pomeroy, R. (2012). *Coral Triangle Regional Ecosystem Approach to Fisheries Management (EAFM) Guidelines DRAFT* (p. 45). Coral Triangle Initiative and USAID Coral Triangle Support Programme.

Reef Check Malaysia (2014). *Dying for Fish Bombing. Does It Really Make Sense?* (p. 4). Kuala Lumpur.

Republic of the Philippines (2009). *National Plan of Action: Republic of the Philippines* (p. 65). Manila.

Saad, J., Hiew, K. & Nagarai, G. (2012). *Review of Malaysian Laws and Policies in Relation to the Implementation of Ecosystem Approach to Fisheries Management in Malaysia* (p. 88). USAID Coral Triangle Support Partnership. Honolulu, Hawaii.

Salao, C., Honasan, A. & Sandalo, R. (2007). *Anilao: Paying to Play: The Dive Fees of Mabini and Tingloy. A Case Study on the Philippines* (p. 22). WWF-Philippines. Quezon City, Philippines.

Short, F., Carruthers, T., Dennison, W. & Waycott, M. (2007). Global Seagrass Distribution and Diversity: A Bioregional Model. *Journal of Experimental Marine Biology and Ecology* 350 (1–2), pp. 3–20.

Sidangoli, M., Lloyd, D. & Boyd, W. E. (2013). Institutional Challenges to the Effectiveness of Management of Bunaken National Park, North Sulawesi, Indonesia. *Asia Pacific Viewpoint* 54 (3), pp. 372–87.

Siry, H. Y. (2011). In Search of Appropriate Approaches to Coastal Zone Management in Indonesia. *Ocean & Coastal Management* 54 (6), pp. 469–77.

Spalding, M. D., Ravilious, C. & Green, E. P. (2001). *World Atlas of Coral Reefs. Prepared at the UNEP World Conservation Monitoring Centre* (p. 432). University of California Press. Berkeley, USA.

Stobutzki, I. C., Silvestre, G. T., Abu Talib, A., Krongprom, A., Supongpan, M., Khemakorn, P., Armada, N. & Garces, L. R. (2006). Decline of Demersal Coastal Fisheries Resources in Three Developing Asian Countries. *Fisheries Research* 78 (2–3).

Syofyanto, H., Farjariyanto, Y. & Koliham, Y. (2011). *Laporan akhir: Pemetaan Partisipatif Taman Nasional Perairan Laut Sawu* (p. 127). Yayasan Pengembangan Pesisir dan Laut and The Nature Conservancy. Kupang, Indonesia.

Tubbataha Protected Area Management Board (2011). *Management Plan of the Tubbataha Reefs Natural Park* (p. 31). Puerto Princessa, Philippines.

United Nations Development Programme (2012). *Arnavon Community Marine Conservation Area Management Committee, Solomon Islands* (p. 12). Equator Initiative Case Study Series. New York, NY.

United Nations Development Programme (2012). *Bunaken National Park Management Advisory Board, Indonesia* (p. 13). Equator Initiative Case Study Series. New York, NY.

United Nations Development Programme (2013). *Tetepare Descendants' Association: Equator Initiative Case Studies* (p. 12). Equator Initiative Case Study Series. New York, NY.

Veron, J. E. N., Devantier, L. M., Turak, E. & Green, A. L. (2009). Delineating the Coral Triangle. *Galaxea, Journal of Coral Reef Studies* 11, pp. 91–100.

Wallace, A. R. (1869). *The Malay Archipelago* (2011, 2nd edn, p. 522). John Beaufoy Publishing. Oxford, United Kingdom.

Ward, T., Tarte, D., Hegerl, E. & Short, K. (2002). *Ecosystem-based Management of Marine Fisheries Policy Proposals and Operational Guidance of Marine Capture Fisheries. WWF Report* (p. 80). WWF Australia. Canberra.

Wilson, J., Darmawan, A., Subijanto, J., Green, A. & Sheppard, S. (2011). *Scientific Design of a Resilient Network of Marine Protected Areas Lesser Sunda Ecoregion, Coral Triangle* (p. 92). The Nature Conservancy. Asia Pacific Marine Program. Report 2/11.

Wood, L. J., Fish, L., Laughren, J. & Pauly, D. (2008). Assessing Progress Towards Global Marine Protection Targets: Shortfalls in Information and Action. *Oryx* 42 (03), pp. 340–51.

WWF-Malaysia (n.d.). S.O.S.: Save Our Seafood. Accessed 12 May 2014 from www.saveourseafood.my

INDEX

ACKNOWLEDGEMENTS

The authors would like to thank the following people and organizations: Fareea Ma (APE Malaysia); Cheryl Madeja, Natasha Yapp (Treasure Images); Ken Scriven, Robecca Jumin (WWF-Malaysia); Rui Pinto (Conservation International, Timor Leste), James Turner (Timor Leste Backpackers), Hans van Rijn (Sailboat ALK), Skippy H. T. (Indonesia and Timor Leste), Wem Turupadan (Kupang, Universitas Nusa Cendana), Yusuf Fajarianto (TNC-Indonesia), Stephanie Lecoeur, Dana Cleary (Dive Timor), Demetrio do Amaral de Carvalho (Haburas Foundation, Dili, Timor Leste), Merry Bako, Aries Timo (Tourism Officer, Pulau Rote, Ba'a), Melkianus Manu (Fisheries Officer, Pulau Rote, Ba'a), Romy and Anne Trono (Bontoc in Batangas Bed and Breakfast), Mavic Matillano (WWF-Philippines), Luli and Luigi Bernas (Philippines), Dr Affendi Yang Amri, Dr Jillian Ooi, Nina Ho (University Malaya), Professor Dr Abdul Latiff Mohamed (Universiti Kebangsaan Malaysia), Joel Palma (WWF-Philippines), Tingo Leve, Shannon Seeto, Salome Topo (WWF-Solomon Islands), Danny and Kerrie Kennedy (Dive Gizo), Dr Ann Marie Schwartz, Faye Siota, Zelda Hilly (World Fish Centre), Nualti Venny, Tastre Ataria (GELCA, Gizo, Solomon Islands), Katrina Moore (Gizo, Solomon Islands), Bruno Manale (Gizo, Solomon Islands), Aquila Maike (Shortland Islands, Solomon Islands), Max Benjamin, Gary Kulisek (Walindi Plantation Resort), Nellie Bau, Adolphna Luvogit (Mahonia Na Dari), Nick Rau (Talasea, West New Britain), Newell Sinaigawi (Department of Fisheries, West New Britain PNG), Sander and Norma Van Den Ende, Yanding Tomda (New Britain Palm Oil), Theresa Rueger (James Cook University), Dr Jeff and Sylvia Kinch (National Fisheries College, Papua New Guinea), Dietmar and Ange Amon (Lissenung Island Resort), Paul Kewter (Digicell), John Aini (Ailan Awareness), Shaun Keane (Nusa Island Retreat), Annisah Sapul, Dr Sven Frijlink (Wildlife Conservation Society, PNG), Jackie Thomas, Paolo Mangahas (WWF Coral Triangle Programme), Joe Kata, Mark Schreffler (WWF Papua New Guinea), Ambassador and Mme Pascal Maubert (France), Tubbataha Protected Area Management Board, Dr Nathan Badenoch, Dinita Setyawati (Kyoto University), Wawan Ridwan, Anton Wijorano, Abdullah Habibi, Yusuf Mooy (WWF-Indonesia), Dr Stuart Campbell (WCS Indonesia), Dr Lida Pet Soede, Dr Jose 'Jingles' Ingles (WWF-International); Helen Brunt (WorldFish Centre), Maurice Knight (USAID), Dr Nicolas Pilcher (Marine Research Foundation), Bo Macao, Ali Bin Thalit and the Koç family.

First published in the United Kingdom in 2014 by John Beaufoy Publishing, 11 Blenheim Court, 316 Woodstock Road, Oxford OX2 7NS, UK
www.johnbeaufoy.com

Copyright © 2014 John Beaufoy Publishing Limited
Copyright © 2014 in text Ken Kassem
Copyright © 2014 in cartography John Beaufoy Publishing Limited
Copyright © 2014 in photographs Eric Madeja, except as listed below
The authors asserts their moral rights to be identified as the authors of this work.

ISBN 978-1-909612-22-8

Text by Ken Kassem
Photographs by Eric Madeja
Designed by Glyn Bridgewater
Edited by Krystyna Mayer
Cartography by William Smuts
Project management by Rosemary Wilkinson

Printed and bound in Singapore by Tien Wah Press (Pte) Ltd

Credits:
Shutterstock/LauraD (p. 37); Bo Macao (p. 65, bottom); Shutterstock/Shane Gross (p. 75, bottom); Shutterstock/Efired (p. 162); Ali Bin Thalit (p. 167); Dr Nicolas Pilcher (p. 185). Maps on page 22 recreated with permission from Bert Hoeksema.

Cover captions and credits
Front cover: Clownfish live symbiotically with anemone species © Eric Madeja. Back cover: Anthias, cup corals and featherstars typical of Anilao © Eric Madeja.